Glencoe Science

BIOLOGY

The
Dynamics
of Life

Unit 5 Resources
Change Through Time

Glencoe

New York, New York   Columbus, Ohio   Chicago, Illinois   Peoria, Illinois   Woodland Hills, California

A GLENCOE PROGRAM
BIOLOGY: THE DYNAMICS OF LIFE

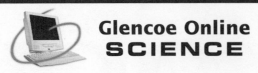

Glencoe Online
SCIENCE

Visit the Glencoe Science Web site
bdol.glencoe.com

You'll find:
Standardized Test Practice, Interactive
Tutor, Section and Chapter Self-Check
Quizzes, Online Student Edition, Web
Links, Microscopy Links, WebQuest
Projects, Internet BioLabs, In the News,
Textbook Updates, Teacher Bulletin
Board, Teaching Today

and much more!

 **Glencoe**

The McGraw-Hill Companies

Send all inquiries to:
Glencoe/McGraw-Hill
8787 Orion Place
Columbus, OH 43240-4027

ISBN 0-07-860216-5

Printed in the United States of America.

2 3 4 5 6 7 8 9 10   009   08 07 06 05 04

Contents

This unit-based booklet contains resource materials to help you teach this unit more effectively. You will find in chapter order:

Reproducible Pages

Hands-on Activities

MiniLab and BioLab Worksheets: Each activity in this book is an expanded version of each BioLab or MiniLab that appears in the Student Edition of *Biology: The Dynamics of Life*. All materials lists, procedures, and questions are repeated so that students can read and complete a lab in most cases without having a textbook on the lab table. Data tables are enlarged so that students can record data in them. All lab questions are reprinted with lines on which students can write their answers. In addition, for student safety, all appropriate safety symbols and caution statements have been reproduced on these expanded pages. Answer pages for each MiniLab and BioLab are included in the Teacher Support and Planning section at the back of this book.

Real World BioApplications: These two-page activities provide students with the opportunity to explore a technological or everyday application of biology. Each activity is directly related to a major concept in the Student Edition, and several examine principles from the physical sciences that underlie the biology content. While some activities are more hands-on, all require critical thinking and creativity. The teaching notes in the Teacher Support and Planning section at the back of this book suggest chapters and topics with which to correlate the activities, explain the purpose of each activity, offer materials tips and teaching strategies, and provide answers to all questions on the student pages.

Extension and Intervention

Reinforcement and Study Guide in English and Spanish: These pages help students understand, organize, and compare the main biology concepts in the textbook. The questions and activities also help build strong study and reading skills. There are four study guide pages for each chapter and two pages for the BioDigest. Students will find these pages easy to follow because the section titles match those in the textbook. Italicized sentences in the study guide direct students to the related topics in the text.

The *Reinforcement and Study Guide* exercises employ a variety of formats including short-answer questions, multiple-choice, matching, true/false, ordering, labeling, completion, and short essay. The clear, easy-to-follow exercises and the self-pacing format are geared to build your students' confidence in understanding biology. The English pages are followed immediately by the study guide pages in Spanish.

Concept Mapping: The *Concept Mapping* worksheets reinforce and extend the graphic organizational skills introduced in the Skill Handbook in the Student Edition of *Biology: The Dynamics of Life*. Concept maps are visual representations of relationships among particular concepts. By using these worksheets, students will gain experience with three different types of concept maps: the *network tree*, which shows causal information, group hierarchies, and branching procedures; the *events chain*, which describes the stages of a process, the steps in a linear procedure, or a sequence of events; and the *cycle map*, which shows how a series of events interacts to produce a set of results again and again.

There is one *Concept Mapping* worksheet for each chapter in the Student Edition. Each worksheet is geared toward a specific section or sections in the chapter so that you can assign it at the most relevant time. An entire section may be mapped or just a few key concepts from the section. Answers to all *Concept Mapping* worksheets are provided in the Teacher Support and Planning section at the back of this book.

Critical Thinking/Problem Solving: For each chapter of **Biology: The Dynamics of Life,** a one-page *Critical Thinking* or *Problem Solving* worksheet is provided to extend the material in the Student Edition. Each worksheet is geared to a specific section or sections in the chapter so that you can assign it at the most relevant time. Answers to all worksheets are provided in the Teacher Support and Planning section at the back of this book.

The worksheets follow Bloom's taxonomy of problem solving. Each worksheet tests the students' abilities on one or more of the following areas:

- to use knowledge

- to comprehend what that knowledge means

- to apply that knowledge to a new but related situation

- to analyze the different aspects of new information

- to synthesize new information in order to respond to a particular situation in a creative and logical way

Transparency Activity Masters

Section Focus Transparencies: A *Section Focus Transparency* is provided for every section in the Student Edition. Each transparency contains two questions related to the transparency image. In addition, each transparency is reproduced as a master in this book. These masters are designed to generate interest and focus students' attention on the topic being presented in that section. Teaching strategies background information, and possible answers to the questions for each transparency in this unit can be found in the Teacher Support and Planning section at the back of this book.

Basic Concepts Transparencies: This book contains a blackline master version of each color *Basic Concepts Transparency* for this unit. In most cases, the transparency illustration is different than the illustration in the textbook, providing optimum support for your visual learners. The accompanying worksheet for each transparency master focuses students' attention on the topic, requiring them to analyze the illustration and relate it to the concepts being taught in the textbook. The use of the masters makes the worksheets convenient homework assignments.

Teaching strategies as well as worksheet answers are provided for each transparency. Several transparencies utilize overlays for maximum teaching benefit, and explanations of how to use these overlays are included in the teaching suggestions in the Teacher Support and Planning section at the back of this book.

Reteaching Skills Transparencies: This book contains a blackline master version of each color *Reteaching Skills Transparency* for this unit. The transparencies and masters provide visual tools for reteaching important concepts. To make your reteaching more powerful, the transparencies and masters are developed around basic skills. These skills include, but are not limited to, interpreting scientific illustrations, sequencing, recognizing cause and effect, comparing and contrasting, observing and inferring, and classifying.

The accompanying worksheet for each transparency master focuses students' attention on the topic skill. Students may find it helpful to take notes on the master and use it as a study tool for the chapter. Teaching strategies as well as worksheet answers are provided for each transparency. Several transparencies utilize overlays for maximum teaching benefit, and explanations of how to use these overlays are included in the teaching suggestions in the Teacher Support and Planning section at the back of this book.

Assessment

Chapter Assessment: These worksheets provide materials to assess your students' understanding of concepts from each chapter in this unit. Each chapter test includes several sections that assess students' understanding at different levels.

The *Reviewing Vocabulary* section tests students' knowledge of the chapter's vocabulary. A variety of formats is used, including matching, multiple-choice, and completion.

The *Understanding Main Ideas* section consists of two parts. Part A tests recall and basic understanding of facts presented in the chapter. Part B is designed to be more challenging and requires deeper comprehension of concepts than does Part A. Students may be asked to explain biological processes and relationships or to make comparisons and generalizations.

The *Thinking Critically* section requires students to use several high-order learning skills. For some questions, students will need to interpret data and discover relationships presented in graphs and tables. Other questions may require them to apply their understanding of concepts to solve problems, to compare and contrast situations, and to make inferences or predictions.

In the final section, *Applying Scientific Methods*, students are put into the role of researcher. They may be asked to read about an experiment, simulation, or model, and then apply their understanding of chapter concepts and scientific methods to analyze and explain the procedure and results. Many of the questions in this section are open-ended, giving students the opportunity to demonstrate both reasoning and creative skills. This section, as well as the other sections of each test, begins on a separate page, so that if you wish to omit a section from a test, you can easily do so.

Answers or possible responses to all questions for the chapters in this unit are provided in the Teacher Support and Planning section at the back of this book.

Student Recording Sheet: *Student Recording Sheets* allow students to use the Chapter Assessments in the Student Edition as a practice for standardized testing, giving them an opportunity to use bubble answer grids and number grids for recording answers. There is a recording sheet for each chapter in this unit and a recording sheet for the Unit Assessment at the end of the BioDigest for this unit. Answers for the *Student Recording Sheets* can be found in the side wrap of the Teacher Wraparound Edition on the Chapter Assessment and Unit Review pages.

Teacher Support and Planning

Foldables™ Study Organizer: These pages provide an additional Foldables strategy for each chapter in this unit. The strategy is presented at the top of the page along with more challenging options or suggestions for students who prefer their Foldables to be more creative or informative. The bottom of the page provides instructions for how to make Foldables and can be reproduced and distributed to students who may benefit from the illustrated instructions.

Teacher Guide and Answers: Answers or possible answers for questions in this booklet can be found in chapter order in this section. Materials, teaching strategies, and content background along with chapter references are found where appropriate.

Contents

Chapter 14 The History of Life

MiniLab 14.1   Marine Fossils

Observing and Inferring

Certain sedimentary rocks are formed totally from the fossils of once-living ocean organisms called diatoms. The diatom fossils are often 1000 meters thick. These sedimentary rocks were at one time in the past under ocean water and were then lifted above sea level during periods of geological change.

Procedure

1. Prepare a wet mount of a small amount of diatomaceous earth. **CAUTION:** *Use care in handling microscope slides and coverslips. Do not breathe in dry diatomaceous earth.*
2. Examine the material under low-power magnification.
3. Draw several of the different shapes you see.
4. Compare the shapes of the fossils you observe to present-day diatoms shown in the photograph. Remember, however, that the fossils you observe are probably only pieces of the whole organism.

Analysis

1. Describe the appearance of fossil diatoms.

_____

_____

2. How are fossil diatoms similar to and different from the diatoms in the photo? Can you use these similarities and differences to predict how diatoms have changed over time? Explain your answer.

_____

_____

_____

3. What part of the original diatom did you observe under the microscope? How did this part survive millions of years? Why were the fossils you observed in pieces?

_____

_____

_____

MiniLab 14.2   A Time Line

Organizing Data

In this activity, you will construct a time line that is a scale model of the geologic time scale. Use a scale in which 1 meter equals 1 billion years. Each millimeter then represents 1 million years.

Procedure

1 Use a meterstick to draw a continuous line down the middle of a 5 m strip of adding-machine tape.

2 At one end of the tape, draw a vertical line and label it "The Present."

3 Measure off the distance that represents 4.6 billion years ago. Draw a vertical line at that point and label it "Earth's Beginning."

4 Using the table below, plot the location of each event on your time line. Label the event and the number of years ago it occurred.

Geologic Time Scale			
Event	**Estimated years ago**	**Event**	**Estimated years ago**
Earliest evidence of life	3.4 billion	First birds	150 million
Paleozoic Era begins	543 million	Cretaceous Period begins	144 million
First land plants	443 million	Dinosaurs become extinct	65 million
Mesozoic Era begins	248 million	Cenozoic Era begins	65 million
Triassic Period begins	248 million	Primates appear	65 million
Jurassic Period begins	206 million	Humans appear	200 000
First dinosaurs	225 million		

Analysis

1. Which era is the longest? The shortest?

2. In which eras did dinosaurs and mammals appear on Earth?

3. What major group first appeared after dinosaurs became extinct?

Chapter 14

INVESTIGATE BioLab

Determining a Rock's Age

PREPARATION

Problem
How can you simulate radioactive half-life?

Objectives
In this BioLab you will:
- **Formulate models** Simulate the radioactive decay of K-40 into Ar-40 with pennies.
- **Collect data** Collect data to determine the amount of K-40 present after several half-lives.

- **Make and use a graph** Graph your data and use its values to determine the age of rocks.

Materials
shoe box with lid
100 pennies
graph paper

Skill Handbook
Use the **Skill Handbook** if you need additional help with this lab.

PROCEDURE

1. Use the data table below.
2. Place 100 pennies in a shoe box.
3. Arrange the pennies so that their "head" sides are facing up. Each "head" represents an atom of K-40, and each "tail" an atom of Ar-40.

4. Record the number of "heads" and "tails" present at the start of the experiment. Use the row marked "0" in the data table.
5. Cover the box. Then shake the box well. Let the shake represent one half-life of K-40, which is 1.3 billion years.

Data Table

Number of Shakes (half-lives)	Number of Heads (K-40 atoms left)				
	Trial 1	**Trial 2**	**Trial 3**	**Totals**	**Average**
0					
1					
2					
3					
4					
5					

6. Remove the lid and record the number of "heads" you see facing up. Remove all the "tail" pennies.
7. To complete the first trial, repeat steps 5 and 6 four more times.
8. Run two more trials and determine an average for the number of "heads" present at each half-life.

9. Draw a full-page graph. Plot your average values on the graph. Plot the number of half-lives for K-40 on the *x*-axis and the number of "heads" on the *y*-axis. Connect the points with a line. Remember, each half-life mark on the graph axis for K-40 represents 1.3 billion years.
10. **Cleanup and Disposal** Return everything to its proper place for reuse. Wash hands thoroughly.

INVESTIGATE BioLab **Determining a Rock's Age,** *continued*

ANALYZE AND CONCLUDE

1. **Applying Concepts** What symbol represented an atom of K-40 in this experiment? What symbol represented an atom of Ar-40?

_____

_____

2. **Thinking Critically** Compare the numbers of protons and neutrons of K-40 and Ar-40. (Consult the Periodic Chart in the Appendix for help.) Can Ar-40 change back to K-40? Explain your answer, pointing out what procedural part of the experiment supports your answer.

_____

_____

3. **Defining Operationally** Define the term half-life. What procedural part of the simulation represented a half-life period of time in the experiment?

_____

_____

_____

4. **Communicating** Explain how scientists use radioactive dating to approximate a rock's age.

_____

_____

_____

5. **Making and Using Graphs** You are attempting to determine the age of a rock sample. Use your graph to read the rock's age if it has:

   a. 70% of its original K-40 amount.

_____

   b. 35% of its original K-40 amount.

_____

   c. 10% of its original K-40 amount.

6. **Error Analysis** Could the size of the box and how vigorously the box was shaken introduce errors into the data? Explain.

Chapter 14 — The History of Life

In your textbook, read about the early history of Earth.

For each statement below, write <u>true</u> or <u>false</u>.

_____ **1.** Earth is thought to have formed about 4.6 billion years ago.

_____ **2.** The conditions on primitive Earth were very suitable for life.

_____ **3.** Geological events on Earth set up conditions that would play a major role in the evolution of life on Earth.

_____ **4.** By the end of the Mesozoic, the continents took on their modern shape.

_____ **5.** The first organisms appeared on land between 3.9 and 3.4 billion years ago.

In your textbook, read about a history in the rocks.

For each statement in Column A, write the letter of the matching item in Column B.

Column A	Column B
_____ **6.** A footprint, trail, or burrow, providing evidence of animal activity	**a.** petrified fossil
_____ **7.** A fossil embedded in tree sap, valuable because the organism is preserved intact	**b.** imprint
_____ **8.** An exact stone copy of an original organism, the hard parts of which have been penetrated and replaced by minerals	**c.** trace fossil
_____ **9.** Any evidence of an organism that lived long ago	**d.** cast
_____ **10.** The fossil of a thin object, such as a leaf or feather, that falls into sediments and leaves an outline when the sediments hardened	**e.** amber-preserved
_____ **11.** An empty space left in rock, showing the exact shape of the organism that was buried and decayed there	**f.** fossil
_____ **12.** An object formed when a mold is filled in by minerals from the surrounding rock	**g.** mold

Chapter
14 **The History of Life,** *continued*

Section 14.1 The Record of Life

In your textbook, read about the age of a fossil.

Answer the following questions.

13. Explain how relative dating works.

_____

_____

_____

14. What is the limitation of relative dating?

_____

15. What dating technique is often used by paleontologists to determine the specific age of a fossil?

_____

16. How do scientists use this dating technique to determine the ages of rocks or fossils?

_____

_____

In your textbook, read about a trip through geologic time.

Complete the table by checking the correct column for each statement.

	Era			
Statement	**Pre-Cambrian**	**Paleozoic**	**Mesozoic**	**Cenozoic**
17. The first photosynthetic bacteria form dome-shaped structures called stromatolites.				
18. Primates evolve and diversify.				
19. Divided into three periods: Triassic, Jurassic, and Cretaceous				
20. An explosion of life, characterized by the appearance of many types of invertebrates and plant phyla				
21. Mammals appear.				
22. Dinosaurs roam Earth, and the ancestors of modern birds evolve.				
23. Flowering plants appear.				
24. Amphibians and reptiles appear.				

Chapter 14 The History of Life, *continued*

In your textbook, read about origins: the early ideas.

Use each of the terms below just once to complete the passage.

microorganisms	vital force	Louis Pasteur	biogenesis
nonliving matter	S-shaped	disproved	Francesco Redi
organisms	broth	microscope	spontaneous generation
spontaneously	air		

Early scientists believed that life arose from **(1)** _____ through a process they called

(2) _____ . In 1668, the Italian physician **(3)** _____ conducted

an experiment with flies that **(4)** _____ this idea. At about the same time, biologists

began to use an important new research tool, the **(5)** _____ . They soon discovered the

vast world of **(6)** _____ . The number and diversity of these organisms was so great that

scientists were led to believe once again that these organisms must have arisen **(7)** _____ .

By the mid-1800s, however, **(8)** _____ was able to disprove this hypothesis once and for

all. He set up an experiment, using flasks with unique **(9)** _____ necks. These flasks

allowed **(10)** _____ , but no organisms, to come into contact with a broth containing

nutrients. If some **(11)** _____ existed, as had been suggested, it would be able to get into

the **(12)** _____ through the open neck of the flask. His experiment proved that organ-

isms arise only from other **(13)** _____ . This idea, called **(14)** _____ ,

is one of the cornerstones of biology today.

Determine if the statement is true. If it is not, rewrite the italicized part to make it true.

15. Biogenesis *explains* how life began on Earth.

_____

16. For life to begin, simple *inorganic* molecules had to be formed and then organized into complex molecules.

_____

17. Several billion years ago, Earth's atmosphere had no free *methane*.

_____

18. Primitive Earth's atmosphere may have been composed of water vapor, carbon dioxide, and *nitrogen*. _____

19. In the early 1900s, Alexander Oparin proposed a widely accepted hypothesis that life began *on land*. _____
_____

20. *Pasteur* hypothesized that many chemical reactions occurring in the atmosphere resulted in the formation of a primordial soup. _____

21. In 1953, Miller and Urey tested Oparin's hypothesis by simulating the conditions of *modern* Earth in the laboratory. _____

22. Miller and Urey showed that organic compounds, including *nucleic acids* and sugars, could be formed in the laboratory, just as had been predicted. _____

23. This "life-in-a-test-tube" experiment of Miller and Urey provides support for some modern hypotheses of *biogenesis*. _____

24. Sidney Fox took Miller and Urey's experiment further and showed how amino acids could cluster to form *protocells*. _____

In your textbook, read about the evolution of cells.

Answer the following questions.

25. Describe the likely characteristics of the first organisms on Earth.
_____
_____
_____

26. What is an autotroph? What factors helped them thrive on Earth?
_____
_____
_____

27. What present-day organisms may be similar to the first autotrophs? Why?
_____
_____

28. What change occurred in Earth's atmosphere after the evolution of photosynthesizing prokaryotes? Why?
_____
_____
_____

Capítulo 14 La historia de la vida

En tu libro de texto, lee acerca de los comienzos de la Tierra.

Indica si cada uno de los enunciados es <u>verdadero</u> o <u>falso</u>.

_____ **1.** Se cree que la Tierra se formó hace aproximadamente 4.6 billones de años.

_____ **2.** Las condiciones de la Tierra primitiva eran muy adecuadas para la vida.

_____ **3.** Los sucesos geológicos ocurridos en la Tierra han producido condiciones que han determinado la evolución de la vida en la Tierra.

_____ **4.** Al final del Mezosoico, los continentes tenían la forma que tienen actualmente.

_____ **5.** Los primeros organismos aparecieron en la Tierra entre 3.9 y 3.5 billones de años atrás.

En tu libro de texto, lee acerca de la historia en las rocas.

Anota la letra de la columna B que corresponda a cada enunciado de la columna A

Columna A	Columna B
_____ **6.** Huella u otro tipo de rastro que muestra pruebas de actividad animal	**a.** fósil petrificado
_____ **7.** Fósil incrustado en resina de árboles, muy valioso porque el organismo se preserva intacto	**b.** impresión
_____ **8.** Copia exacta en roca de un organismo original. Los minerales han penetrado y sustituido las partes duras del organismo	**c.** fósil traza
_____ **9.** Toda prueba de un organismo que vivió hace muchos años	**d.** vaciado
_____ **10.** Fósil que se forma cuando un objeto delgado como una hoja o una pluma, cae en sedimentos, formándose el contorno del objeto cuando los sedimentos se endurecen	**e.** preservación en ámbar
_____ **11.** Espacio vacío en una roca que muestra la forma exacta de un organismo que murió y quedó sepultado en el sitio	**f.** fósil
_____ **12.** Objeto formado cuando un molde se llena con los minerales de las rocas que lo rodean	**g.** molde

En tu libro de texto, lee acerca de la antigüedad de los fósiles.

Contesta las siguientes preguntas.

13. Explica cómo funciona la datación relativa.

_____

_____

_____

14. ¿Cuál es la limitación de la datación relativa?

_____

15. ¿Cuál técnica de datación usan a menudo los paleontólogos para determinar la edad específica de un fósil?

_____

16. ¿Cómo se determina la antigüedad de rocas o fósiles con esta técnica?

_____

_____

En tu libro de texto, lee sobre un viaje a través del tiempo geológico.

Completa la tabla indicando la columna correspondiente a cada enunciado.

	Era			
Enunciado	**Precámbrica**	**Paleozoica**	**Mesozoica**	**Cenozoica**
17. Las primeras bacterias fotosintéticas forman estructuras en forma de domo llamadas estromatolitos.				
18. Los primates evolucionan y se diversifican.				
19. Se divide en tres periodos: Triásico, Jurásico y Cretáceo				
20. Explosión de formas de vida caracterizada por la aparición de muchos tipos de invertebrados y filos de plantas				
21. Aparecen los mamíferos.				
22. Los dinosaurios habitan la Tierra y aparecen los ancestros de las aves modernas.				
23. Aparecen las plantas con flores.				
24. Aparecen los anfibios y reptiles.				

En tu libro de texto, lee sobre el orígen de la vida: las primeras ideas.

Completa el párrafo usando cada término una sola vez.

microorganismos	fuerza vital	**Louis Pasteur**	**biogenesis**
materia inanimada	forma de S	**refutó**	**Francesco Redi**
organismos	caldo	**microscopio**	**generación espontánea**
espontáneamente	aire		

Los primeros científicos creían que la vida había surgido a partir de **(1)** _____ mediante

un proceso que llamaron **(2)** _____ . En 1668, el medico italiano **(3)** _____

realizó un experimento con moscas que **(4)** _____ dicha idea. En esa misma época, los biólo-

gos empezaron a usar una nueva e importante herramienta de investigación: el **(5)** _____ y

pronto descubrieron el vasto mundo de los **(6)** _____ . Su número y diversidad era tan grande

que los científicos empezaron de nuevo a creer que éstos habían surgido **(7)** _____ . Sin

embargo hacia mediados del siglo XIX, **(8)** _____ refutó esta hipótesis de una vez por todas.

Realizó un experimento usando frascos especiales con cuello en **(9)** _____ . Estos frascos per-

mitían la entrada de **(10)** _____ , pero no de microorganismos hasta el caldo rico en nutrien-

tes, dentro de los frascos. Si existía alguna **(11)** _____ como había sido sugerido, ésta podría

llegar al **(12)** _____ a través del cuello sin tapón de los frascos. Este experimento demostró

que los organismos provienen de otros **(13)** _____ . Esta idea, conocida como

(14) _____ , es una de las piedras angulares de la biología actual.

Si el enunciado es verdadero, escribe *verdadero*; de lo contrario, modifica la sección en itálicas para hacer verdadero el enunciado.

15. La biogénesis *explica* cómo empezó la vida en la Tierra.

_____

16. Para que la vida empezara, fue necesario que se formaran moléculas *inorgánicas* simples que después dieron

origen a moléculas más complejas.

_____

17. Hace varios billones de años la atmósfera de la Tierrra no contenía *metano* libre.

_____

18. Es probable que la atmósfera primitiva de la Tierra estuviera compuesta por vapor de agua, dióxido de carbono y *nitrógeno.* _____

19. A principios del siglo XX, Alejandro Oparin propuso la hipótesis, ampliamente aceptada, de que la vida empezó *en tierra.*

_____

20. *Pasteur* formuló la hipótesis de que las reacciones químicas que ocurrieron en la atmósfera originaron la sopa primordial. _____

21. En 1953, Miller y Urey pusieron a prueba la hipótesis de Oparin, simulando las condiciones *modernas* de la Tierra en el laboratorio. _____

22. Miller y Urey demostraron que se pueden obtener compuestos orgánicos en el laboratorio, incluyendo *ácidos nucleicos* y azúcares, como había sido propuesto. _____

23. El experimento de Miller y Urey, "la vida en un tubo de ensayo", sirvió de apoyo para algunas hipótesis modernas sobre *biogénesis.* _____

24. Sidney Fox profundizó los experimentos de Miller y Urey y demostró que los aminoácidos se pueden agrupar y formar *protocélulas.* _____

En tu libro de texto, lee sobre la evolución de las células.

Contesta las siguientes preguntas.

25. Describe las características que probablemente tuvieron los primeros organismos de la Tierra.

_____

_____

_____

26. ¿Qué es un autótrofo? ¿Qué factores les permitieron prosperar en la Tierra?

_____

_____

27. ¿Cuáles organismos actuales probablemente se parezcan a los primeros autótrofos? ¿Por qué?

_____

_____

28. ¿Qué cambio ocurrió en la atmósfera de la Tierra después de la aparición de los procariotas fotosintéticos? ¿Por qué?

_____

_____

_____

Chapter 14 — The History of Life

Use with Chapter 14, Section 14.1

Formation of a Fossil

Make an events chain to show how fossils found in sedimentary rocks are formed, discovered, and dated.

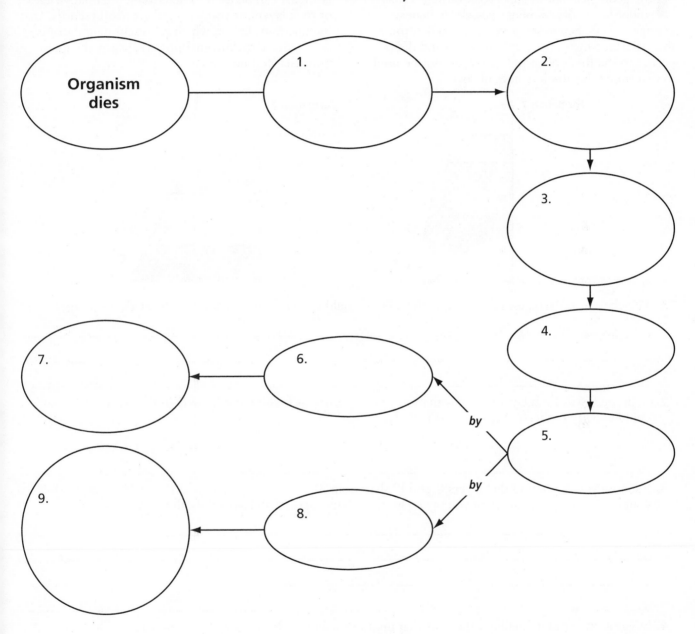

Using the Law of Superposition

The geological law of superposition states that older layers of sedimentary rock lay beneath younger layers. Scientists use this law to determine the order in which organisms appeared and disappeared in the fossil record. The law cannot be used to determine the absolute ages of rock

layers. It can be used to determine the relative ages of rock layers by comparing their fossil records. Use the diagrams below, which represent neighboring sedimentary rock formations, to answer the questions that follow.

Formation 1

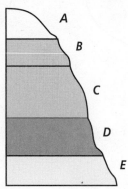

Formation 2

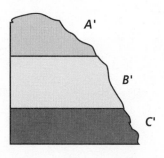

1. Which layer is the oldest in each formation? How would you know if these two layers are the same age?

_____

_____

_____

2. Suppose fossils from layer C' in Formation 2 are the same as fossils from layer D in Formation 1. What could you say about the age of fossils from Layer E?

_____

_____

3. Suppose you also found that layers C and B' shared similar fossils. Layers B and A' look very similar, but contain no fossils. What could you say about the relative ages of all layers of both formations?

_____

_____

_____

4. Suggest one or more geological events that might explain why Formation 2 has fewer layers than Formation 1.

_____

_____

_____

Master
35   **Inferring from Fossils**

Use with Chapter 14, Section 14.1

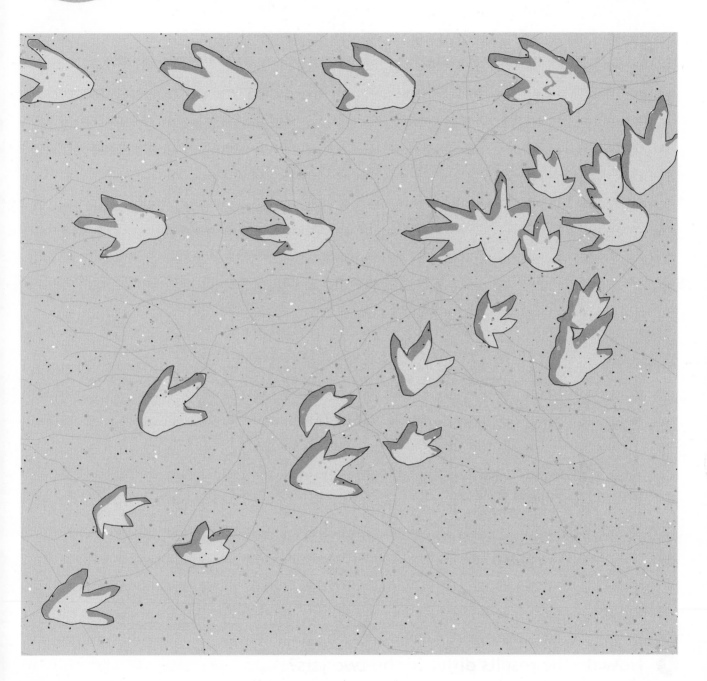

❶ The diagram shows a set of fossilized footprints. What observations can you make about the footprints?

❷ What can you infer from the observations?

Master
36 **Redi's Experiment**

Use with Chapter 14, Section 14.2

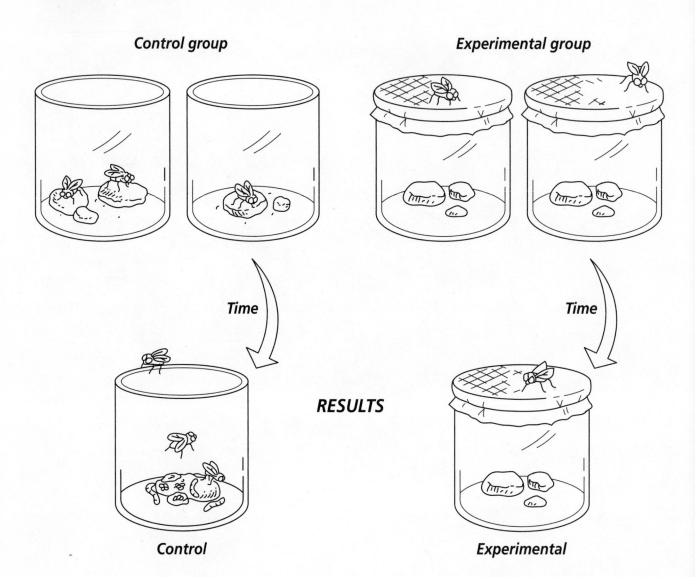

Control group

Experimental group

Time

Time

RESULTS

Control

Experimental

❶ How do the results differ in the two jars?

❷ What might you conclude from these results?

Master 20 **Pasteur's Experiment**

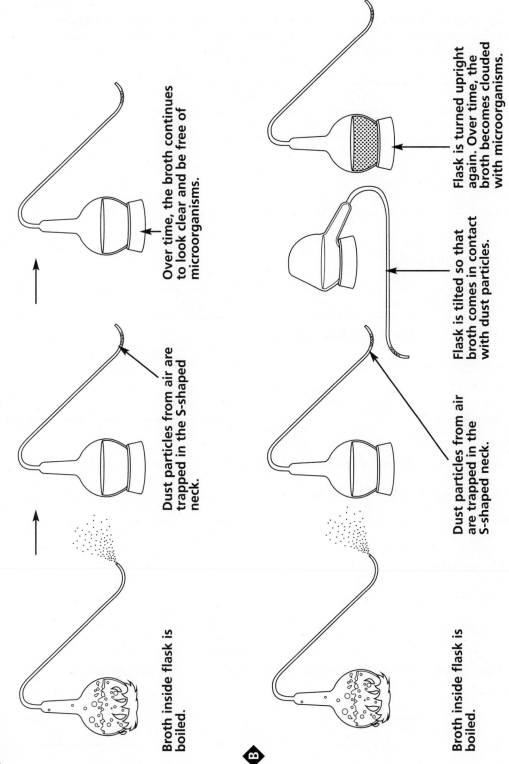

A

Broth inside flask is boiled.

Dust particles from air are trapped in the S-shaped neck.

Over time, the broth continues to look clear and be free of microorganisms.

B

Broth inside flask is boiled.

Dust particles from air are trapped in the S-shaped neck.

Flask is tilted so that broth comes in contact with dust particles.

Flask is turned upright again. Over time, the broth becomes clouded with microorganisms.

Worksheet 20 Pasteur's Experiment

Use with Chapter 14, Section 14.2

1. The transparency provides a simplified illustration of Pasteur's experiments to disprove the idea that microorganisms arise spontaneously from a vital force in the air. Study Flasks A and B. How do they differ?

_____

_____

_____

_____

2. What is the independent variable?

_____

_____

3. What is the dependent variable?

_____

_____

4. Why are both flasks heated to the boiling point?

_____

_____

_____

_____

5. Does Pasteur's experiment disprove the idea of spontaneous generation? Explain.

_____

_____

_____

6. What might be a control for this experiment?

_____

_____

_____

7. If Pasteur's experiment disproves spontaneous generation, what hypothesis does it support?

_____

_____

_____

Master 23

Geologic Time Scale

ERA	PERIOD	MILLION YEARS AGO (approximate)	MAJOR EVOLUTIONARY EVENTS	MAJOR LIFE FORMS
Cenozoic	Quaternary		Humans evolve	
Cenozoic		1.8		
Cenozoic	Tertiary		Mammals dominant	
Cenozoic		65		
Mesozoic	Cretaceous		Flowering plants appear	
Mesozoic		144		
Mesozoic	Jurassic		First birds First flowering plants	
Mesozoic		206		
Mesozoic	Triassic		First mammals First dinosaurs	
		248		
Paleozoic	Permian		Conifers appear	
Paleozoic		290		
Paleozoic	Carboniferous	323	First reptiles First seed plants	
Paleozoic		354		
Paleozoic	Devonian		First amphibians	
Paleozoic		417		
Paleozoic	Silurian			
Paleozoic	Ordovician	443	First fishes	
Paleozoic	Cambrian	491	First vertebrates	
		543		
	Precambrian		Invertebrates	
		1800	Eukaryotes	
		3500	Prokaryotes	
		4000	Life evolves	

Worksheet 23 — Geologic Time Scale

1. What is the basis of the geologic time scale?

_____

_____

2. Describe the divisions of the geologic time scale.

_____

_____

3. During what era and at approximately what date does fossil evidence suggest life had evolved on Earth? What form of life was this?

_____

_____

4. What forms of living things characterized the Cambrian Period?

_____

_____

5. During what era did the first vertebrates evolve? What were these vertebrates?

_____

_____

6. The dinosaurs and many other species became extinct in a relatively short period of time that marks what is called the K-T boundary, which stands between the Cretaceous and Tertiary Periods. About how long ago did the dinosaurs become extinct?

_____

_____

7. Imagine you found a fossil of a bird that dates to 213 million years. Why would this find be astonishing to scientists?

_____

_____

8. Suppose a geologist finds a layer of rock that can be dated to 320 million years ago. Layers from which periods would be expected to be above and below the newly discovered layer?

_____

_____

Reviewing Vocabulary

Complete the paragraph by writing the correct term on the appropriate line. Use these choices:

archaebacteria	fossils	protocells
biogenesis	plate tectonics	spontaneous generation

From ancient times until recently, it was believed that living organisms could arise from nonliving

materials. This belief is referred to as **(1)** _____ . According to the three-century-

old writings of Jean Van Helmont, if a dirty shirt and grains of wheat are placed in a container and left for

21 days, mice will form from the fermenting wheat. With the invention of the microscope and careful

experimentation, it has been reasonably proven that life arises only from life. This idea is referred to as

(2) _____ . The oldest organisms of which scientists have any record are approxi-

mately 3.4 billion years old. **(3)** _____ provide evidence of such organisms. The

question of how the first unicellular organisms were produced from inorganic materials is a problem

scientists are still studying. One possible answer is that conditions on the ancient Earth led to the

formation of organized structures that carried out some life activities. These structures, called

(4) _____ , were capable of growth and division. After much time, they evolved

into heterotrophic prokaryotes. Over more time, organisms evolved that could synthesize food from inor-

ganic raw materials. These organisms were probably similar to today's prokaryotes that survive in harsh

conditions without oxygen. These organisms are known as **(5)** _____ .

The geological activity of Earth has influenced the development of organisms. For example, at the

beginning of the Mesozoic Era, the modern continents were merged into one large landmass. The landmass

broke into individual continents that moved apart. The theory that explains how the continents moved is

called **(6)** _____ . As the continents moved apart, descendants of organisms living

on the continents may have experienced different climates because of the new locations of the continents.

Chapter 14 The History of Life, *continued*

Understanding Main Ideas (Part A)

In the space at the left, write the letter of the word or phrase that best completes the statement or answers the question.

_____ **1.** A clear fish imprint in a rock indicates that the rock is probably

    a. volcanic.   **b.** sedimentary.   **c.** metamorphic.   **d.** igneous.

_____ **2.** Which fact is the basis for using the fossil record as evidence for the order of evolution?

    a. In undisturbed layers of rock strata, the older fossils are found in the deeper layers.

    b. There are fossils of all life forms to be found in rock layers.

    c. All fossils were formed at the same time.

    d. Fossils have been shown to provide a complete record of human evolution.

_____ **3.** A theory concerning the origin of life states that Earth's ancient atmosphere contained

    a. water vapor, carbon dioxide, and nitrogen.

    b. water vapor, oxygen, and hydrogen.

    c. methane, ammonia, and oxygen.

    d. methane, carbon dioxide, and oxygen.

_____ **4.** Which group of organisms is believed to have been the earliest to evolve?

    a. land plants   **b.** cyanobacteria   **c.** aquatic dinosaurs   **d.** mammals

_____ **5.** According to one theory, the first prokaryotes probably obtained their food

    a. through the synthesis of organic molecules from inorganic molecules.

    b. through a combination of photosynthesis and aerobic respiration.

    c. by eating carbohydrates formed by autotrophs.

    d. by consuming organic molecules available in their environment.

_____ **6.** Entire organisms, with even their most delicate parts intact, have been found preserved in

    a. igneous rock formations and ice.

    b. mineral deposits and metamorphic rock.

    c. amber and ice.

    d. amber and mineral deposits.

_____ **7.** While looking for fossils on an eroded hillside, you discover fossil coral and fish in one layer. In a layer just above, you find the fossil imprint of a fern frond and some fossil moss. Assuming the rock has not been disturbed, which of the following is the most probable conclusion?

    a. The area had been a sea until recent times.

    b. A forest had once grown there but had become submerged by water.

    c. A sea had been replaced by land in ancient times.

    d. A saltwater sea had changed to a freshwater lake in ancient times.

Understanding Main Ideas (Part B)

In the space at the left, write the letter of the word or phrase that best completes the statement or answers the question.

_____ **1.** Which event contributed most directly to the evolution of aerobic organisms?

    a. an increase in the concentration of methane in the ancient atmosphere

    b. a decrease in the sun's light intensity

    c. the presence of organisms able to carry on photosynthesis

    d. an increase in the number of organisms carrying on fermentation

_____ **2.** Urey and Miller subjected water, ammonia, methane, and hydrogen to heating and cooling cycles and jolts of electricity in an attempt to

    a. determine how the dinosaurs became extinct.

    b. find out whether the conditions of ancient Earth could have formed complex organic compounds.

    c. determine the age of microfossils.

    d. find out how ozone forms in the atmosphere.

Answer the following questions.

3. Explain the role of plate tectonics in the theory of continental drift.

_____

_____

_____

_____

4. Explain the relationship between early photosynthetic autotrophs and the eventual rise of aerobic life forms.

_____

_____

_____

_____

Thinking Critically

Read the paragraph below. Then answer the questions that follow.

Radioactive isotopes, atoms with unstable nuclei, decay over time, giving off radiation as they break down. The decay rate of every radioactive element is known; moreover, radioactive decay continues at a steady rate. Scientists compare the amount of the original radioactive element to the amount of the new element present, which has formed as a result of the decay. Suppose that you start with 100 grams of a certain radioisotope that decays to half its original amount in 50 000 years.

1. Complete the following table so that the amount of parent material (original radioisotope) and the amount of daughter material (nonradioactive end product) are correct for the number of years that have passed.

Amount of Parent Material	Amount of Daughter Material	Years That Have Passed
100 grams	0 grams	0
1.	**5.**	50 000
2.	**6.**	100 000
3.	**7.**	150 000
4.	**8.**	200 000
3.125 grams	96.875 grams	250 000

2. On the following grid, graph the data in your table in order to show the relationship between the passage of time and the amount of original radioisotope. (Consider the time 0 as that point at which the decay of the full amount of the isotope begins. The 250 000-year point is the present time.)

Years Passed vs. Amount of Radioisotope

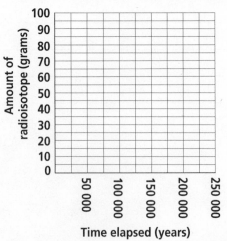

Applying Scientific Methods

Examine the illustration of rock strata and fossil remains recorded by a paleobiologist who was studying rock layers located at the base of a mountain. Then answer the questions that follow.

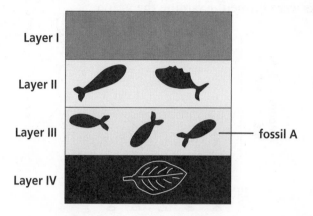

1. Assuming that the oldest of the strata is layer IV and that the youngest is layer I, name and describe two techniques that could be used to determine the age of fossil A.

_____

_____

_____

_____

_____

_____

_____

_____

_____

2. Based on the fossil record, explain what has happened to the type of habitat found in the area as time passed.

_____

_____

_____

_____

_____

_____

_____

Chapter
14 The History of Life, *continued*

Applying Scientific Methods *continued*

Through a chemical analysis of the rock layers represented in the illustration on the previous page and of other, deeper layers, scientists were able to construct a graph of the amount of oxygen present in the atmosphere when the rocks were formed. Examine the graph.

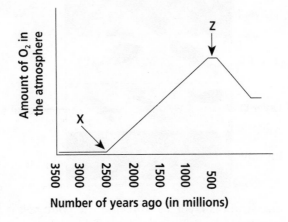

3. Describe what major event occurred in the evolution of life on Earth at point X that is directly related to the change in the graph above.

_____

_____

4. How did this event affect the level of oxygen in the atmosphere?

_____

_____

5. What major evolutionary event occurred at the point on the graph indicated by Z?

_____

6. How did this event affect the oxygen level?

_____

7. What could paleontologists look for to confirm your answers to questions 3 and 6?

_____

_____

Chapter 14 Assessment
Student Recording Sheet

Chapter Assessment

Use with pages 390–391 of the Student Edition

Vocabulary Review

Write the vocabulary words that match the definitions in your book.

1. _____   3. _____

2. _____   4. _____

Understanding Key Concepts

Select the best answer from the choices given and fill in the corresponding oval.

5. Ⓐ Ⓑ Ⓒ Ⓓ

6. Ⓐ Ⓑ Ⓒ Ⓓ

7. Ⓐ Ⓑ Ⓒ Ⓓ

8. Ⓐ Ⓑ Ⓒ Ⓓ

9. Ⓐ Ⓑ Ⓒ Ⓓ

Constructed Response

Record your answers for Questions 10–12 on a separate sheet of paper.

Thinking Critically

Record your answers for Questions 13, 15, 16, and 17 on a separate sheet of paper.

14. **REAL WORLD BIOCHALLENGE** Follow your teacher's instructions for presenting your BioChallenge answer.

Standardized Test Practice

The Princeton Review

Part 1   Multiple Choice

Select the best answer from the choices given and fill in the corresponding oval.

18. Ⓐ Ⓑ Ⓒ Ⓓ

19. Ⓐ Ⓑ Ⓒ Ⓓ

20. Ⓐ Ⓑ Ⓒ Ⓓ

21. Ⓐ Ⓑ Ⓒ Ⓓ

22. Ⓐ Ⓑ Ⓒ Ⓓ

23. Ⓐ Ⓑ Ⓒ Ⓓ

Part 2
Constructed Response/Grid In

Record your answers for Questions 24 and 25 on a separate sheet of paper.

Contents

Chapter 15 The Theory of Evolution

Chapter 15

MiniLab 15.1

Formulating Models

Camouflage Provides an Adaptive Advantage

Camouflage is a structural adaptation that allows organisms to blend with their surroundings. In this activity, you'll discover how natural selection can result in camouflage adaptations in organisms.

Procedure

1 Working with a partner, punch 100 dots from a sheet of white paper with a paper hole punch. Repeat with a sheet of black paper. These dots will represent black and white insects.

2 Scatter both white and black dots on a sheet of black paper.

3 Decide whether you or your partner will role-play a bird.

4 The "bird" looks away from the paper, then turns back, and immediately picks up the first dot he or she sees.

5 Repeat step 4 for one minute.

Analysis

1. What color dots were most often collected?

_____

_____

2. How does color affect the survival rate of insects?

_____

_____

_____

3. What might happen over many generations to a similar population in nature?

_____

_____

_____

MiniLab
15.2 Detecting a Variation

Collecting Data

Pick almost any trait—height, eye color, leaf width, or seed size—and you can observe how the trait varies in a population. Some variations are an advantage to an organism and some are not.

Procedure

1 Copy the data table shown here, but include the lengths in millimeters (numbers 25 through 45) that are missing from this table.

Data Table											
Length in mm	20	21	22	23	24	–	46	47	48	49	50
Checks											
My Data—Number of shells											
Class Data—Number of shells											

2 Use a millimeter ruler to measure a peanut shell's length. In the Checks row, check the length you measured.

3 Repeat step 2 for 29 more shells.

4 Count the checks under the length and enter the total in the row marked My Data.

5 Use class totals to complete the row marked Class Data.

Analysis

1. Was there variation among the lengths of peanut shells? Use specific class totals to support your answer.

_____

_____

2. If larger peanut shells were a selective advantage, would this be stabilizing, directional, or disruptive selection? Explain your answer.

_____

_____

_____

_____

Natural Selection and Allelic Frequency

Chapter **15**

Problem
How does natural selection affect allelic frequency?

Objectives
In this BioLab, you will:
- **Simulate** natural selection by using beans of two different colors.
- **Calculate** allelic frequencies over five generations.
- **Demonstrate** how natural selection can affect allelic frequencies over time.
- **Use the Internet** to collect and compare data from other students.

Materials
colored pencils (2)
paper bag
graph paper
pinto beans
white navy beans

Safety Precautions
CAUTION: *Clean up spilled beans immediately to prevent anyone from slipping.*

Skill Handbook
Use the **Skill Handbook** if you need additional help with this lab.

1. Use the data table.
2. Place 50 pinto beans and 50 white navy beans into the paper bag.
3. Shake the bag. Remove two beans. These represent one rabbit's genotype. Set the pair aside, and continue to remove 49 more pairs.
4. Arrange the beans on a flat surface in two columns representing the two possible rabbit phenotypes, gray (genotypes *GG* or *Gg*) and white (genotype *gg*).
5. Examine your columns. Remove 25 percent of the gray rabbits and 100 percent of the white rabbits. These numbers represent a random selection pressure on your rabbit population. If the number you calculate is a fraction, remove a whole rabbit to make whole numbers.
6. Count the number of pinto and navy beans remaining. Record this number in your data table.

7. Calculate the allelic frequencies by dividing the number of beans of one type by 100. Record these numbers in your data table.
8. Begin the next generation by placing 100 beans into the bag. The proportions of pinto and navy beans should be the same as the percentages you calculated in step 7.
9. Repeat steps 3 through 8, collecting data for five generations.
10. Go to **bdol.glencoe.com/internet_lab** to post your data.
11. Graph the frequencies of each allele over five generations. Plot the frequency of the allele on the vertical axis and the number of the generation on the horizontal axis. Use a different colored pencil for each allele.
12. **Cleanup and Disposal** Return all materials to their proper places for reuse.

Natural Selection and Allelic Frequency, continued

Data Table

Generation	Allele G			Allele g		
	Number	Percentage	Frequency	Number	Percentage	Frequency
Start	50	50	0.50	50	50	0.50
1						
2						
3						
4						
5						

ANALYZE AND CONCLUDE

1. Analyze Data Did either allele disappear? Why or why not?

_____

_____

2. Think Critically What does your graph show about allelic frequencies and natural selection?

_____

_____

3. Infer What would happen to the allelic frequencies if the number of eagles declined?

_____

_____

4. Error Analysis Explain any differences in allelic frequencies you observed between your data and the data from the Internet. What advantage is there to have a large amount of data? What problems might there be in using data from the Internet?

_____

_____

Chapter
15 The Theory of Evolution

In your textbook, read about Charles Darwin and natural selection.

For each statement, write <u>true</u> or <u>false</u>.

_____ **1.** H.M.S. *Beagle*, upon which Charles Darwin served as naturalist, set sail on a collecting and mapping expedition in 1831.

_____ **2.** The environments that Darwin studied exhibited little biological diversity.

_____ **3.** By careful anatomical study, Darwin found that the many species of plants and animals on the Galápagos Islands were unique and bore no relation to species seen in other parts of the world.

_____ **4.** The tortoises of the Galápagos Islands are among the largest on Earth.

_____ **5.** After returning to England, Darwin studied his collections for 10 years.

_____ **6.** Darwin named the process by which evolution proceeds *artificial selection*.

You are a naturalist who traveled to the Galápagos Islands. Below are excerpts from field notes. Next to each set of notes, write a heading. Use these choices: Overproduction of Offspring, Natural Selection, Struggle for Existence, Variation.

7.
| **Field Notes** |
| Female finches found on the Galápagos Islands lay enormous numbers of eggs. |
| _____ |

8.
| **Field Notes** |
| These finches compete for a particular species of insect that inhabits the small holes found in tree bark. |
| _____ |

9.
| **Field Notes** |
| Some finches' beaks are long, some are short. The finches with long beaks are better adapted to remove the insects from the bark. |
| _____ |

10.
| **Field Notes** |
| The finches with the long beaks survive and produce greater numbers of offspring with long beaks. |
| _____ |

Chapter
15   The Theory of Evolution, *continued*

Reinforcement and Study Guide

Section 15.1 Natural Selection and the
Evidence for Evolution

In your textbook, read about natural selection and adaptations.

Identify the type of structural adaptation that the statement describes. If the statement applies to both, write <u>both</u>. Use these choices: mimicry, camouflage, both.

_____ **11.** Enable(s) an organism to blend in with its surroundings

_____ **12.** Provide(s) protection for an organism by copying the appearance of another species

_____ **13.** The coloration of a flounder that allows the fish to avoid predators

_____ **14.** Involve(s) changes to the external appearance of an organism

_____ **15.** A flower that looks like a female bee

In your textbook, read about evidence for evolution.

Complete the chart by checking the kind of evidence described.

Evidence	Type of Evidence				
	Homologous Structure	**Analogous Structure**	**Vestigial Structure**	**Embryological Development**	**Genetic Comparisons**
16. A modified structure seen among different groups of descendants					
17. In the earliest stages of development, a tail and pharyngeal pouches can be seen in fish, birds, rabbits, and mammals.					
18. Exemplified by forelimbs of bats, penguins, lizards, and monkeys					
19. Eyes in a blind fish					
20. DNA and RNA comparisons may lead to evolutionary trees.					
21. Bird and butterfly wings have same function but different structures					
22. A body structure reduced in original function but may have been used in an ancestor					

Chapter 15 The Theory of Evolution, continued

Section 15.2 Mechanisms of Evolution

In your textbook, read about population genetics and evolution.

Determine if the statement is true. If it is not, rewrite the italicized part to make it true.

1. *Adaptations* of species are determined by the genes contained in the DNA code. _____

2. When Charles *Mendel* developed the theory of natural selection in the 1800s, he did not include a genetic explanation. _____

3. Natural selection can act upon an individual's *genotype*, the external expression of genes. _____

4. Natural selection operates on *an individual* over many generations. _____

5. The entire collection of genes among a population is its *gene frequency*. _____

6. If you know the *phenotypes* of all the organisms in a population, you can calculate the allelic frequency of the population. _____

7. A population in which frequency of alleles *changes* from generation to generation is said to be in genetic equilibrium. _____

8. A population that is in *genetic equilibrium* is not evolving. _____

9. Any factor that affects *phenotype* can change allelic frequencies, thereby disrupting the genetic equilibrium of populations. _____

10. Many *migrations* are caused by factors in the environment, such as radiation or chemicals, but others happen by chance. _____

11. Mutations are *important* in evolution because they result in genetic changes in the gene pool. _____

12. Genetic *equilibrium* is the alteration of allelic frequencies by chance processes. _____

13. Genetic drift is more likely to occur in *large* populations. _____

14. The factor that can significantly change the genetic equilibrium of a population's gene pool is *mutation*. _____

15. The type of natural selection by which one of the extreme forms of a trait is favored is called *disruptive selection*. _____

In your textbook, read about the evolution of species.

Complete each statement.

16. _____ can occur only when either interbreeding or the production of fertile offspring is prevented among members of a population.

17. _____ occurs when formerly interbreeding organisms are prevented from producing fertile offspring.

18. Polyploid speciation is perhaps the fastest form of speciation because it results in immediate

_____ .

19. The hypothesis that species originate through a slow buildup of new adaptations is known as

_____ .

20. This hypothesis is supported by evidence from the _____ record.

21. The hypothesis of _____ states that speciation may occur rapidly.

In your textbook, read about patterns of evolution.

Answer the following questions.

22. What happened to the ancestor of the honey creeper when it left the mainland and encountered the diverse niches of Hawaii?

_____

_____

23. What is adaptive radiation?

_____

_____

24. Adaptive radiation is one example of divergent evolution. When does divergent evolution occur?

_____

_____

_____

25. When will convergent evolution occur?

_____

_____

Capítulo 15 La teoría de la evolución

En tu libro de texto, lee sobre Charles Darwin y la selección natural.

Indica si cada enunciado es verdadero o falso.

_____ **1.** El barco H.M.S. *Beagle*, donde Charles Darwin sirvió como naturalista, partió en una expedición de recopilación y cartografía en 1831.

_____ **2.** Los ambientes que Darwin estudió exhibían muy poca diversidad biológica.

_____ **3.** Después de cuidadosos estudios anatómicos, Darwin descubrió que muchas de las especies de plantas y animales que habitaban las islas Galápagos eran únicas y no tenían ninguna relación con especies de otras partes del planeta.

_____ **4.** Las tortugas de las islas Galápagos se encuentran entre las más grandes de la Tierra.

_____ **5.** Después de su regreso a Inglaterra, Darwin estudió sus colecciones durante 10 años.

_____ **6.** Darwin llamó *selección artificial* al mecanismo mediante el cual actúa la evolución.

Eres un naturalista que viaja a las islas Galápagos. A continuación, se muestran fragmentos de notas de campo. En la linea correspondiente, anota el título de cada nota. Usa las siguientes opciones: Sobreproducción de crías, Selección natural, Lucha por la existencia y Variabilidad.

7.
> **Notas de campo**
>
> Los pinzones hembra que habitan en las islas Galápagos depositan grandes cantidades de huevos.
>
> _____

8.
> **Notas de campo**
>
> Estos pinzones compiten por una especie particular de insectos que habitan pequeños agujeros en la corteza de árboles.
>
> _____

9.
> **Notas de campo**
>
> El pico de algunos pinzones es largo, otros tienen pico corto. Los pinzones de pico largo están mejor adaptados para alcanzar los insectos en los hoyos de la corteza.
>
> _____

10.
> **Notas de campo**
>
> Las aves de pico largo sobreviven y producen un mayor número de crías de pico largo.
>
> _____

La teoría de la evolución, *continuación*

Sección 15.1 La selección natural y las pruebas de la evolución

En tu libro de texto, lee sobre la selección natural y las adaptaciones.

Identifica el tipo de adaptación estructural descrito en cada enunciado. Si el enunciado se aplica a ambas, escribe <u>ambas</u>. Usa estas opciones: mimetismo, camuflaje o ambas.

_____ **11.** Permite a un organismo mezclar su apariencia con la del ambiente

_____ **12.** Protege a un organismo al copiar la apariencia de otra especie

_____ **13.** Coloración de un lenguado que le permite escapar de los depredadores

_____ **14.** Incluye cambios en la apariencia de un organismo

_____ **15.** Flor que semeja una abeja hembra

En tu libro de texto, lee sobre las pruebas de la evolución.

Completa la tabla indicando el tipo de prueba descrita.

Prueba	Tipo de prueba				
	Estructura homóloga	Estructura análoga	Estructura vestigial	Desarrollo embrionario	Comparación genética
16. Estructura modificada presente en los diferentes grupos de descendientes					
17. En las primeras etapas del desarrollo se pueden observar cola y bolsas faríngeas en peces, aves, conejos y mamíferos.					
18. Un ejemplo son las extremidades anteriores de murciélagos, pingüinos, lagartijas y monos					
19. Ojos en un pez ciego					
20. Las comparaciones de DNA y de RNA ayudan a obtener árboles evolutivos.					
21. Las alas de aves y mariposas tienen la misma función, pero diferente estructura					
22. Estructura corporal de función original reducida y usada tal vez por algún antepasado					

Capítulo 15 La teoría de la evolución, *continuación*

Sección 15.2 Los mecanismos de la evolución

En tu libro de texto, lee sobre la genética demográfica y evolutiva.

Si el enunciado es verdadero, escribe *verdadero*; **de lo contrario, modifica la sección en itálicas para hacer verdadero el enunciado.**

1. Los genes contenidos en el DNA determinan las *adaptaciones* de las especies. _____

2. Cuando Charles *Mendel* desarrolló su teoría de la selección natural, no incluyó una explicación genética. _____

3. La selección natural actúa sobre el *genotipo* del individuo, es decir, la expresión corporal de los genes.

_____

4. La selección natural actúa sobre *un individuo* a lo largo de muchas generaciones. _____

5. La *frecuencia génica* se refiere a todos los genes de una población. _____

6. Si conoces los *fenotipos* de todos los organismos de una población, puedes calcular sus frecuencias alélicas. _____

7. Se dice que la población cuyas frecuencias alélicas *cambian* de generación en generación, está en equilibrio genético. _____

8. Las poblaciones en *equilibrio genético* no evolucionan. _____

9. Todos los factores que afectan el *fenotipo* afectan las frecuencias alélicas, rompiendo así el equilibrio genético de las poblaciones. _____

10. Muchas *migraciones* son ocasionadas por factores ambientales como la radiación o las sustancias químicas, pero otras ocurren aleatoriamente. _____

11. Las mutaciones son *importantes* para la evolución porque producen cambios genéticos en el caudal de genes. _____

12. El *equilibrio* genético es el cambio aleatorio de las frecuencias alélicas. _____

13. Es más probable que la deriva génica ocurra en poblaciones *grandes*. _____

14. El factor que puede significativamente cambiar el equilibrio genético del caudal de genes de una población es la *mutación*. _____

15. El tipo de selección natural que favorece una de las formas extremas de un rasgo se conoce como *selección disruptiva*. _____

En tu libro de texto, lee sobre la evolución de especies.

Completa cada enunciado.

16. La _____ puede ocurrir si surgen mecanismos que eviten el cruce o la generación de progenie fértil entre los miembros de la población.

17. El _____ ocurre cuando se interrumpe la generación de progenie fértil entre organismos que anteriormente tenían progenie fértil.

18. La especiación poliploide es quizás la forma más rápida de especiación porque produce _____ inmediato.

19. La hipótesis de que las especies se originan debido a la acumulación de nuevas adaptaciones se conoce como _____ .

20. Las pruebas del registro _____ apoyan esta hipótesis.

21. La hipótesis del _____ establece que la especiación puede ocurrir rápidamente.

En tu libro de texto, lee sobre los patrones de la evolución.

Contesta las siguientes preguntas.

22. ¿Qué le ocurrió al ancestro del ave azucarera cuando salió de tierras continentales y se encontró con los diferentes nichos de Hawai?

_____

_____

23. ¿Qué es la radiación adaptativa?

_____

_____

24. La radiación adaptativa es un ejemplo de evolución divergente. ¿Bajo qué condiciones ocurre la evolución divergente?

_____

_____

25. ¿Bajo qué condiciones ocurre la evolución convergente?

_____

Evidence of Evolution

Complete the concept map on evidence of evolution. Use these words or phrases once: *anatomy, embryology, fossils, fossil bones, homologous structures, nucleotide sequences.*

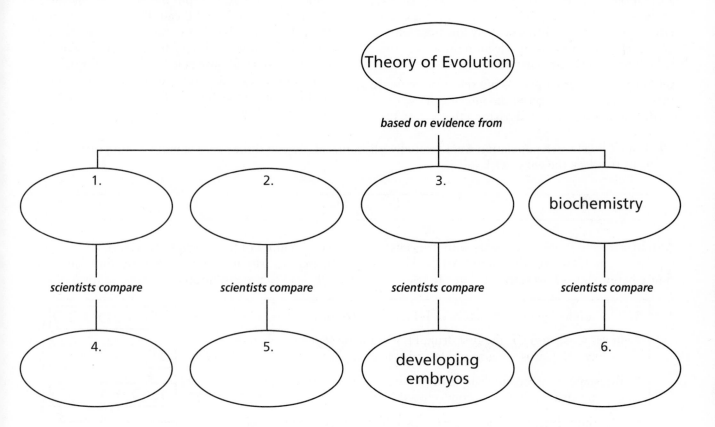

Chapter
15 The Theory
of Evolution

Selection Pressures

Selection pressures are those factors in the environment of a population that favor certain adaptations. Selection pressures result in the survival of those population members that possess these adaptations and make survival less likely for those who do not have them. In this way, selection pressures contribute to evolutionary changes.

Of interest to microbiologists is a selection pressure that developed as a result of the long-term use of medication designed to kill bacteria that cause TB.

When the drug isoniazid is used to kill TB bacteria, enzymes in a TB cell normally cause the isoniazid molecules to split; the split molecules are harmful to the membrane of the TB cell. Destroying the membrane kills the TB cell. In one mutation of the TB bacteria, however, this enzyme is deleted, which renders the isoniazid molecule harmless. Eventually, only molecules resistant to the drug survive and multiply, and a new strain of drug-resistant TB bacteria evolves.

1. If no TB cells in a population were treated with isoniazid, do you think there would be more or fewer TB cells that lack the enzyme? Explain.

_____

_____

A similar selection pressure occurs with drugs used to control the HIV virus that causes AIDS. The figure below shows how scientists hope to use a combination of three drugs, AZT, ddI, and pyridinone, as a trio of selection pressures that will eventually lead to the evolution of a harmless form of HIV.

1. The original genetic structure of HIV looks like this.

2. In response to AZT, the first drug, HIV's genetic sequence changes. Even so, the virus remains viable and able to replicate.

3. Resistance to a second drug, ddI, requires another mutation, but still the virus is able to reproduce itself.

4. The third drug, pyridinone, provokes a final mutation, which, with the previous changes, robs the virus of its ability to replicate.

2. HIV-infected people often experience relief of symptoms for about two years after beginning to take AZT. Then the symptoms often return. Use what you know about selection pressures to explain this phenomenon.

_____

_____

3. Why do you think people taking AZT are sometimes switched to the drug ddI when HIV symptoms return?

_____

4. Those who first take AZT and then ddI often develop a third mutation of the virus, resistant to both drugs. Scientists have learned, however, that when the genetic sequence of a virus mutates several times, the virus often loses its ability to replicate. Why might combining three drugs prove effective?

_____

_____

Master
37 Camouflage

Use with Chapter 15, Section 15.1

*Snowshoe hare
in summer*

Snowshoe hare in winter

❶ What is the advantage of this snowshoe hare's seasonal color change?

❷ The adaptation that allows an animal to blend in with its environment is called camouflage. What examples of camouflage are you familiar with?

Master
38 Evolving Populations

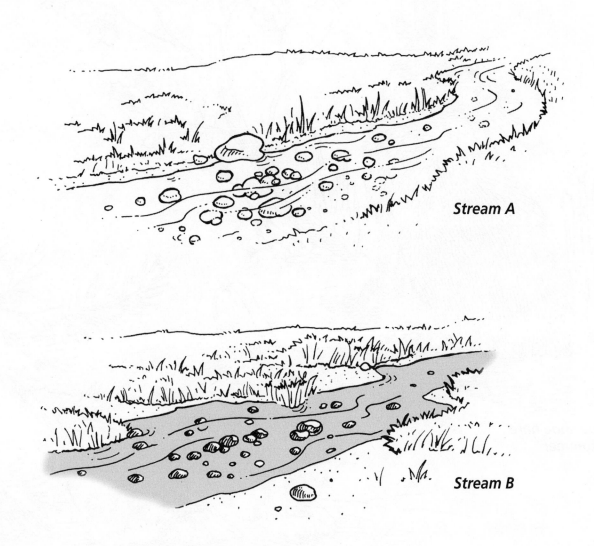

Stream A

Stream B

1 Stream A and Stream B are located on two isolated islands with similar characteristics. How do these two stream beds differ?

2 Suppose a fish that varies in color from a lighter shade to a darker shade is introduced from Stream A into Stream B. How might the color of the fish population in Stream B change over time?

Master 21

Genetic Equilibrium

	Allele frequency	Phenotype frequency
First generation	$R = 0.75$ $R' = 0.25$	White = 0 Pink = 0.5 Red = 0.5
Second generation	$R = 0.75$ $R' = 0.25$	White = 0.125 Pink = 0.25 Red = 0.625

First generation genotypes: RR', RR, RR', RR, RR', RR', RR', RR

Second generation genotypes: RR, RR, R'R', RR, RR', RR, RR', RR

Worksheet 21

Genetic Equilibrium

1. What is the pattern of heredity shown in the transparency?

_____

_____

_____

2. Explain why this pattern of heredity is useful in illustrating genetic equilibrium.

_____

_____

_____

_____

3. How does the first generation differ from the second generation?

_____

_____

_____

4. Why is the population of snapdragons shown in the transparency considered to be in genetic equilibrium?

_____

_____

5. Would the population shown in the transparency be considered to be evolving or not evolving? Explain your answer.

_____

_____

_____

6. How would genetic drift affect a population in genetic equilibrium?

_____

_____

_____

7. What is the impact of mutation on genetic equilibrium?

_____

_____

_____

Master 22

Basic Concepts

Variation in Populations

Use with Chapter 15, Section 15.2

Stabilizing Selection

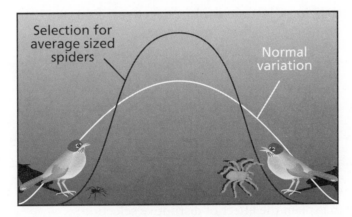

Directional Selection

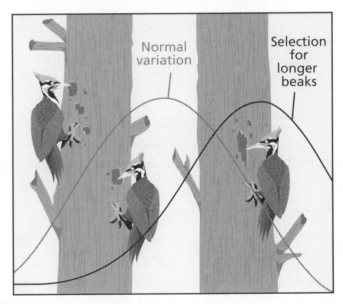

Disruptive Selection

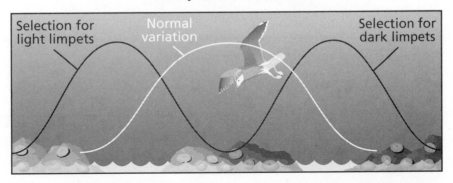

Worksheet 22 **Variation in Populations**

Use with Chapter 15, Section 15.2

1. Study the graph for stabilizing selection. Explain the effect of this type of natural selection.

_____

_____

2. Use the transparency to explain the effect of directional selection.

_____

_____

_____

3. Use the transparency to explain the effect of disruptive selection.

_____

_____

_____

4. Why might average-sized spiders be favored in a given environment?

_____

_____

_____

5. Why might woodpeckers with longer beaks have a selective advantage over those with shorter beaks?

_____

_____

_____

6. Limpets are marine organisms that attach themselves to rocks. Under what environmental conditions might intermediate forms of limpets—those that are tan, rather than white or dark brown—be at a disadvantage?

_____

_____

7. What do the three types of natural selection have in common?

_____

_____

_____

Master 24   **Role of Isolation in Speciation**

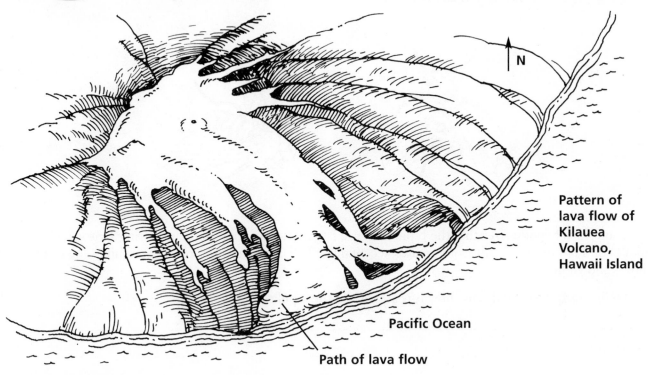

Pattern of lava flow of Kilauea Volcano, Hawaii Island

Pacific Ocean

Path of lava flow

Source: Volcano Watching, Hawaii Natural History Dept. & US Dept. of Interior.

Creation of a *Kipuka*—an isolated area

Picture-winged *Drosophila*

Size: Similar to common housefly

Inversions in gene sequences

Species 1

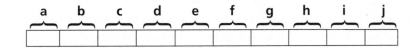

| a | b | c | d | e | f | g | h | i | j |

Species 2

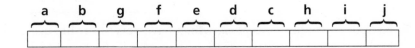

| a | b | g | f | e | d | c | h | i | j |

Species 3

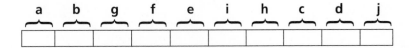

| a | b | g | f | e | i | h | c | d | j |

Worksheet 24

Role of Isolation in Speciation

Use with Chapter 15, Section 15.2

Ken Kaneshiro hypothesizes that the rapid increase in genetic variation in picture-wing *Drosophila* in kipukas on Hawaii may result from greater acceptance of changes in the steps in courtship. One of the steps is shown here.

1. Define *speciation* and discuss how it is at work in the kipukas.

_____

_____

_____

2. Define *geographic isolation* and discuss how it is at work in the kipukas.

_____

_____

3. Define *reproductive isolation* and discuss how it is at work in the kipukas.

_____

_____

4. On the transparency, you can see a series of genes for three species of organisms. Explain what has happened to the genes. How could this change lead to a separate species?

_____

_____

_____

5. Kaneshiro studies *Drosophila*, which have very short life cycles. Birds also live within the kipukas. Form a hypotheses to explain why Kaneshiro would decide not to study birds.

_____

_____

Chapter 15 The Theory of Evolution

Reviewing Vocabulary

Write the word or phrase that best completes the statement. Use these choices:

adaptive radiation	vestigial structure	punctuated equilibrium
mimicry	natural selection	gene pool
polyploid	stabilizing selection	camouflage
genetic drift	artificial selection	allelic frequency

1. _____ is a technique in which the breeder selects particular traits.

2. A structural adaptation enabling an organism to blend in with its environment is

   _____ .

3. Another structural adaptation called _____ protects an organism by copying

   the appearance of another species.

4. The total number of genes present in a population is the _____ .

5. The _____ is the percentage of a particular allele in a population.

6. The alteration of allelic frequencies by chance events is known as _____ .

7. _____ is the type of selection that favors average individuals in a population.

8. Any species with a multiple set of chromosomes is known as a(n) _____ .

9. _____ is a mechanism for change in a population in which organisms with

   favorable variations live, reproduce, and pass on their favorable traits.

10. The concept that speciation occurs relatively quickly with long periods of stability in between is

    known as _____ .

11. Any structure that no longer serves it original function in a living organism but may have been used

    in an ancestor is known as a(n) _____ .

12. The evolution of an ancestral species into an array of species that occupy different niches is called

    _____ .

Understanding Main Ideas (Part A)

In the space at the left, write the letter of the word or phrase that best completes the statement.

_____ **1.** Natural selection can best be defined as the

    a. survival of the biggest and strongest organisms in a population.

    b. elimination of the smallest organisms by the biggest organisms.

    c. survival and reproduction of the organisms that occupy the largest area.

    d. survival and reproduction of the organisms that are genetically best adapted to the environment.

_____ **2.** Structures that have a similar embryological origin and structure but are adapted for different purposes, such as a bat wing and a human arm, are called

    a. embryological structures.   **b.** analogous structures.

    c. homologous structures.   **d.** homozygous structures.

_____ **3.** Mutations such as polyploidy and crossing over provide the genetic basis for

    a. evolution.   **b.** spontaneous generation.

    c. biogenesis.   **d.** sexual reproduction.

_____ **4.** Within a decade of the introduction of a new insecticide, nearly all of the descendants of the target pests were immune to the usual-sized dose. The most likely explanation for this immunity to the insecticide is that

    a. eating the insecticide caused the bugs to become resistant to it.

    b. eating the insecticide caused the bugs to become less resistant to it.

    c. it destroyed organisms that cause disease in the insects, thus allowing them to live longer.

    d. it selected random mutations that were present in the insect population and that provided immunity to the insecticide.

_____ **5.** The flying squirrel of North America very closely resembles the flying phalanger of Australia. They are similar in size, have long, bushy tails, and skin folds that allow them to glide through the air. The squirrel is a placental mammal, while the phalanger is a marsupial. These close resemblances, even though genetically and geographically separated by great distances, can best be explained by

    a. convergent evolution.   **b.** divergent evolution.

    c. spontaneous generation.   **d.** vestigial structures.

_____ **6.** Hawaiian honeycreepers are a group of birds with similar body shape and size. However, they vary greatly in color and beak shape. Each species occupies its own niche and is adapted to the foods available in its niche. The evolution from a common ancestor to a variety of species is an example of

    a. divergent evolution.   **b.** cross-pollination.

    c. vegetative propagation.   **d.** convergent evolution.

Chapter Assessment

Chapter 15 The Theory of Evolution, *continued*

Understanding Main Ideas (Part B)

In the space at the left, write the letter of the word or phrase that best completes the statement or answers the question.

_____ **1.** Which of the following is *not* a factor that causes changes in the frequency of homozygous and heterozygous individuals in a population?

    a. mutations   **b.** migration   **c.** random mating   **d.** genetic drift

_____ **2.** When checking shell color for a species of snail found only in a remote area seldom visited by humans, scientists discovered the distribution of individuals that is shown in the graph.

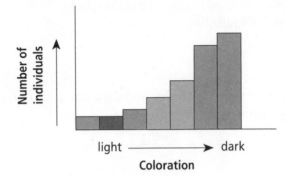

Based on the information shown in the graph, the snail population is undergoing

    a. stabilizing selection.   **b.** disruptive selection.

    c. artificial selection.   **d.** directional selection.

_____ **3.** The theory of continental drift hypothesizes that Africa and South America slowly drifted apart after once being a single landmass. The monkeys on the two continents, although very similar, show numerous genetic differences. Which factor is probably the most important in maintaining these differences?

    a. comparative anatomy   **b.** comparative embryology

    c. geographic isolation   **d.** fossil records

_____ **4.** Which combination of characteristics in a population would provide the *greatest* potential for evolutionary change?

    a. small population, few mutations   **b.** small population, many mutations

    c. large population, few mutations   **d.** large population, many mutations

_____ **5.** Upon close examination of the skeleton of an adult python, a pelvic girdle and leg bones can be observed. These features are an example of

    a. artificial selection.   **b.** homologous structures.

    c. vestigial structures.   **d.** comparative embryology.

_____ **6.** Mutations occur because of

    a. the introduction of new variations from elsewhere.

    b. the introduction of new variations through mistakes in DNA replication.

    c. the chance survival and reproduction of new variations.

    d. change in allele or genotype frequencies.

Thinking Critically

Read the information that follows and then answer the questions.
A study of the squirrel population in a large
northern city revealed that many of the
squirrels inhabited large park areas that
were also populated by numerous squirrel
predators. The graph at the right reflects
the data collected in regard to color and
number of squirrels.

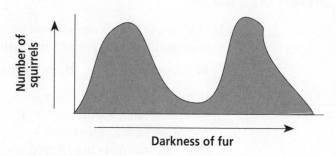

1. Explain why the light- and dark-colored squirrels might be selected for and the medium-colored
   squirrels selected against.

   _____

   _____

   _____

   _____

   _____

   _____

2. Explain how this type of disruptive selection can lead to the separation of this population into two
   distinct species.

   _____

   _____

   _____

   _____

   _____

   _____

   _____

   _____

   _____

   _____

Applying Scientific Methods

A biologist studying a variety of fly in the rain forest noticed that the types of foods the fly preferred were located either high in the trees or in the foliage on the ground. There didn't seem to be any of the preferred foods anywhere in between. An experiment was designed that would select for a genetically determined behavior known as *geotaxis*. If a fly shows positive geotaxis, it flies downward. If the fly shows negative geotaxis, it flies upward.

1. In terms of evolution and natural selection, why would the researcher suspect that the flies being studied would show geotaxis?

_____

_____

_____

To conduct the experiment, the flies being studied were marked and placed in a maze (illustrated below). Each fly was placed in the "start" chamber. To exit from this area, the fly had to make a decision about which of the three exits to enter. One exit faced upward, indicating negative geotaxis, and another exit aimed downward, indicating positive geotaxis. A third exit permitted the fly to remain on middle ground. Each fly was placed in the maze 15 times and its choice of direction recorded. Some flies consistently went upward and entered the food vial at the end of the exit tube. Others consistently went downward and entered the food vial at the lower end. Some flies chose the upward and downward exits equal numbers of times; others went for the middle exit.

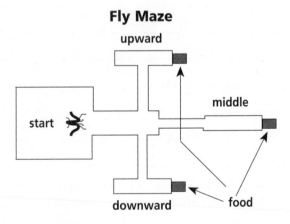

Fly Maze

2. If the selection of direction is a genetic trait, what should happen when flies consistently selecting the upward exit are mated, those selecting the downward exit are mated, and the "no preference" and middle choice flies discarded?

_____

_____

_____

Chapter
15 **The Theory of Evolution,** *continued*

Applying Scientific Methods   *continued*

3. What type of selection pressure is operating in this experiment? Explain your answer.

_____

_____

_____

_____

_____

4. Describe what would be happening to the frequency of the allele for negative geotaxis in the above experiment.

_____

_____

5. What might be acting in the flies' environment to select for flies that do not exhibit a distinct preference for flying upward at every trial or downward at every trial?

_____

_____

_____

_____

_____

_____

_____

6. What might eventually happen if in the wild the flies developed into two populations, with one showing positive geotaxis and the other showing negative geotaxis?

_____

_____

_____

Chapter 15 Assessment
Student Recording Sheet

Vocabulary Review

Write the vocabulary words that match the definitions in your book.

1. _____   3. _____

2. _____   4. _____

Understanding Key Concepts

Select the best answer from the choices given and fill in the corresponding oval.

5. Ⓐ Ⓑ Ⓒ Ⓓ   8. Ⓐ Ⓑ Ⓒ Ⓓ

6. Ⓐ Ⓑ Ⓒ Ⓓ   9. Ⓐ Ⓑ Ⓒ Ⓓ

7. Ⓐ Ⓑ Ⓒ Ⓓ

Constructed Response

Record your answers for Questions 10–12 on a separate sheet of paper.

Thinking Critically

13. **REAL WORLD BIOCHALLENGE** Follow your teacher's instructions for presenting your BioChallenge answer.

Record your answers for Question 14–17 on a separate sheet of paper.

Standardized Test Practice

Part 1   Multiple Choice

Select the best answer from the choices given and fill in the corresponding oval.

18. Ⓐ Ⓑ Ⓒ Ⓓ

19. Ⓐ Ⓑ Ⓒ Ⓓ

20. Ⓐ Ⓑ Ⓒ Ⓓ

21. Ⓐ Ⓑ Ⓒ Ⓓ

22. Ⓐ Ⓑ Ⓒ Ⓓ

Part 2
Constructed Response/Grid In

Record your answers for Questions 23 and 24 on a separate sheet of paper.

Contents

Chapter 16 Primate Evolution

MiniLab 16.1

How useful is an opposable thumb?

Infer

In this activity, you will explore the importance of your thumbs.

Procedure

1 Loosely wrap your dominant hand with tape so that your thumb points in the same direction as your fingers.

2 Try to pick up a pen and write a sentence.

3 Pick up your textbook and hand it to another student.

4 Pitch a tennis ball into an empty trash can two meters away.

5 Repeat steps 2–4 after unwrapping your hand.

Analysis

1. **Compare** Describe the results of your performance with the absence of an opposable thumb and with one.

   _____

   _____

2. **Infer** Why is an opposable thumb an important adaptation for primates?

   _____

   _____

3. **Use Models** Design models for completing three simple tasks without using your thumb, such as turning a doorknob or switching on a light.

   _____

   _____

MiniLab 16.2

Analyzing Information

Compare Human Proteins with Those of Other Primates

Scientists use differences in amino acid sequences in proteins to determine evolutionary relationships of living species. In this activity, you'll compare representative short sequences of amino acids of a protein among other groups of primates to determine their evolutionary history.

Procedure

1. Use the data table below.

2. For each primate listed in the table at right, determine how many amino acids differ from the human sequence. Record these numbers in the data table.

3. Calculate the percentage differences by dividing the numbers by 15 and multiplying by 100. Record the numbers in your data table.

Analysis

1. Which primate is most closely related to humans? Least closely related?

   _____

   _____

2. On another sheet of paper, construct a diagram of primate evolutionary relationships that most closely fits your results.

Table 16.1 Amino Acid Sequences in Primates

Baboon	Chimp	Lemur	Gorilla	Human
ASN	SER	ALA	SER	SER
THR	THR	THR	THR	THR
THR	ALA	SER	ALA	ALA
GLY	GLY	GLY	GLY	GLY
ASP	ASP	GLU	ASP	ASP
GLU	GLU	LYS	GLU	GLU
VAL	VAL	VAL	VAL	VAL
ASP	GLU	GLU	GLU	GLU
ASP	ASP	ASP	ASP	ASP
SER	THR	SER	THR	THR
PRO	PRO	PRO	PRO	PRO
GLY	GLY	GLY	GLY	GLY
GLY	GLY	SER	GLY	GLY
ASN	ALA	HIS	ALA	ALA
ASN	ASN	ASN	ASN	ASN

Data Table

Primate	Amino acids different from humans	Percent difference
Baboon		
Chimpanzee		
Gorilla		
Lemur		

Comparing Skulls of Three Primates

PREPARATION

Problem
How do skulls of primates provide evidence for human evolution?

Objectives
In this BioLab, you will:
- **Determine** how paleoanthropologists study early human ancestors.
- **Compare and contrast** the skulls of australopithecines, gorillas, and modern humans.

Materials
metric ruler
protractor
copy of skull diagrams

Skill Handbook
Use the **Skill Handbook** if you need additional help with this lab.

PROCEDURE

1. Your teacher will provide copies (1/4 natural size) of the skulls of *Australopithecus africanus*, *Gorilla gorilla*, and *Homo sapiens*.

2. The rectangles drawn over the skulls represent the areas of the brain (upper rectangle) and face (lower rectangle). On each skull, determine and record the area of each rectangle (length × width).

3. Measure the diameters of the circles in each

skull. Multiply these numbers by 200 cm². The result is the cranial capacity (brain volume) in cubic centimeters.

4. The two heavy lines projected on the skulls are used to measure how far forward the jaw protrudes. Use your protractor to measure the outside angle (toward the right) formed by the two lines.

5. Complete the data table.

Data Table

	Gorilla	*Australopithecus*	Modern human
1. Face area in cm²			
2. Brain area in cm²			
3. Is brain area smaller or larger than face area?			
4. Is brain area 3 times larger than face area?			
5. Cranial capacity in cm³			
6. Jaw angle			
7. Does lower jaw stick out in front of nose?			
8. Is sagittal crest present?			
9. Is browridge present?			

Comparing Skulls of Three Primates, *continued*

<hr>

ANALYZE AND CONCLUDE

1. Comparing and Contrasting How would you describe the similarities and differences in face-to-brain area in the three primates?

_____

_____

_____

_____

2. Interpreting Observations How do the cranial capacities compare among the three skulls? How do the jaw angles compare?

_____

_____

_____

_____

3. Interpret Data Identify evidence of the change in the species using anatomical similarities.

_____

_____

_____

_____

4. Error Analysis What are the possible sources of error in your analysis?

_____

_____

_____

_____

Primate Skulls for BioLab, Chapter 16

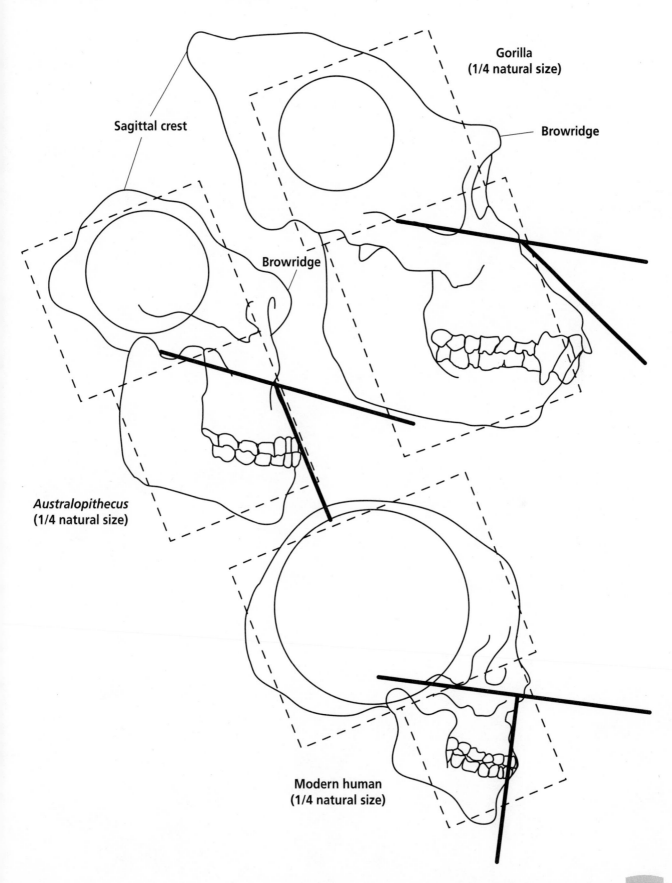

Gorilla
(1/4 natural size)

Sagittal crest

Browridge

Browridge

Australopithecus
(1/4 natural size)

Modern human
(1/4 natural size)

Chapter 16 — Analyzing Lower Back Disorders

Real World BioApplications

An aching back—is it really the price we pay for walking upright? Our earliest primate ancestors probably walked on four feet, just like modern gorillas do today. Humans, however, are *bipedal*, because we walk on two feet. Does this mean back pain is inevitable?

The spine is divided into five vertebral areas: cervical, thoracic, lumbar, sacral, and coccygeal. It is flexible, with pads called discs between the vertebrae, which allow us to bend and twist. It is also naturally curved, which probably helps protect it against injury. It is supported by many muscles, which also help to protect it.

In spite of nature's protection, however, lower back pain is common in humans. It is estimated that more people go to doctors because of back pain than any other complaint besides colds and flu. Some back pain can be attributed directly to injury. Other back pain seems to be brought on through months or years of back stress.

Surprisingly, standing does not cause the hardest stress on the back. Sitting is far worse. Sitting upright at a desk increases disc pressure by 30 to 50 percent. Also, poor muscle control contributes to back strain and pain. Preventing lower back disorders is an important challenge for physical therapists and other health care professionals.

Part A: Body Positions and Stress on the Spine

1. Study the drawings of the gorilla skeleton, the human skeleton, and the human spine. Circle the lumbar area of the spine in the drawing on the right.

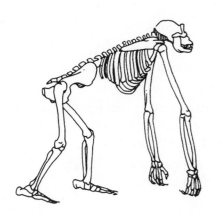  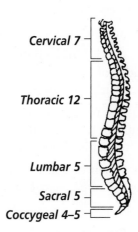

Cervical 7

Thoracic 12

Lumbar 5

Sacral 5

Coccygeal 4–5

2. Look at the side view of the spine in both the gorilla skeleton and the human skeleton. Describe each in terms of how they might curve in the natural "walking" position.

_____

_____

3. Why do you think body positions that put stress on the natural curves of the spine can cause back pain?

_____

4. The lumbar region of the spine supports the most body weight and absorbs the most force. How do you think this contributes to the common complaint of lower back pain?

_____

Chapter 16 Analyzing Lower Back Disorders

Real World BioApplications

Part B: Treatment to Prevent Back Injuries

The list below gives several exercises used by either physical therapists or other exercise professionals. Select six that might be used in an exercise program designed to prevent lower back pain in a patient who is *not* injured. Put an * next to each exercise you "prescribe."

_____ **1.** Stand straight up. Keep your chin parallel to the floor. Turn your head only so you are looking over your right shoulder. Hold. Return your head to the center position. Turn your head over your left shoulder. Hold. Return to center position.

_____ **2.** Lie on your back on the floor with your knees bent and your feet flat on the floor. Cross your arms across your chest. Curl your head and neck slowly toward your knees, lifting your shoulder blades off the floor.

_____ **3.** Lie on your stomach on the floor with your arms bent, hands even with your chest, and palms against the floor. Push straight up with your arms, keeping your hips against the floor.

_____ **4.** Lie on your back on the floor. Slowly pull your knees toward your chest, pulling them with your hands as close to your chest as possible.

_____ **5.** Lie on your back on the floor. Hold one end of a towel in each hand with the middle around the arch of one foot. Keeping both legs straight, use the towel to pull your foot toward the ceiling. Hold. Repeat, using the towel on the other leg.

_____ **6.** Ride an exercise bicycle 30 to 45 minutes every other day.

_____ **7.** Climb up and down five flights of stairs each day or use a stair machine.

_____ **8.** Sit or stand. Hold a lightweight barbell in one hand. Slowly lift the weight to the shoulder of that arm, bending your elbow as you lift, and try to touch your shoulder. Repeat with your other arm.

_____ **9.** Use an exercise machine. Attach yourself to the seat with a seat belt and place your feet in foot pads. Pivot at the waist, slowly pushing back against a bar attached to weights that is almost even with your shoulder blades. Come forward slowly.

_____ **10.** Sit in a chair or use an exercise machine. Fix your lower body in one position. Slowly rotate the upper part of your body, twisting left to right and right to left.

ANALYZE AND CONCLUDE

1. Given the anatomy of the back, why do you think back pain causes many people to stay in bed or greatly limit their physical activity?

_____

_____

2. Review the exercise program you designed for lower back pain. Explain why you chose the exercises you did.

_____

_____

Chapter 16 Primate Evolution

In your textbook, read about the characteristics of a primate.

Complete the chart by checking those structures or functions that are characteristic of primates.

Structure/Function	Primate
1. Round head	
2. Flattened face	
3. Small head	
4. Large relative brain size	
5. Highly developed vision	
6. Poor vision	
7. Binocular vision	
8. Color vision	
9. Color-blind	
10. Vision the dominant sense	
11. Smell the dominant sense	
12. Immobile joints	
13. Flexible shoulder joints	
14. Skeleton adapted for movement among trees	
15. Skeleton adapted for swimming	
16. Hands and feet equipped with claws	
17. Hands and feet equipped with nails	
18. Eyes face to the side	
19. Feet constructed for grasping	
20. Opposable thumbs	

In your textbook, read about primate origins.

For each statement below, write __true__ or __false__.

_____ **21.** Scientists believe that primates evolved about 66,000 years ago.

_____ **22.** The earliest primate may have been a strepsirrhinelike animal called *Purgatorius.*

_____ **23.** Anthropoids are a group of small-bodied primates.

_____ **24.** Strepsirrhines include lemurs and tarsiers.

_____ **25.** Strepsirrhines can be found in the tropical forests of South America.

Chapter 16 **Primate Evolution,** *continued*

Section 16.1 Primate Adaptation and Evolution

Identify the following pictures. Use these choices: baboon, tarsier, spider monkey. Then on the second line write the group that is represented by the picture. Use these choices: New World monkey, Old World monkey, haplorhine.

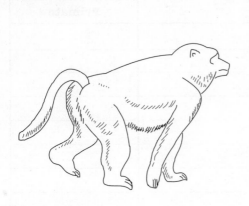

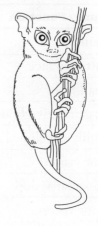

26. _____

_____

27. _____

_____

28. _____

_____

Answer the following questions.

29. What do similarities among monkeys, apes, and humans indicate about their evolution?

_____

_____

30. According to the fossil record, what were the first modern anthropoids to evolve and about when did they evolve?

_____

_____

31. What is the evolutionary history of primates based on?

_____

_____

32. What may have led to the eventual speciation of baboons and other ground-living monkeys?

_____

_____

33. What does DNA analysis of modern hominoids suggest about their evolutionary history?

_____

_____

In your textbook, read about hominids.

Answer the following questions.

1. What is an australopithecine? _____

2. What fossil skull did Raymond Dart discover in Africa in 1924? _____

3. Why was *A. africanus* unlike any primate fossil skull that Dart had ever seen? _____

_____

4. What did the position of the foramen magnum indicate to Dart? _____

_____

Label the following skulls. Use these choices: chimpanzee, human, *A. afarensis*

5. _____   **6.** _____   **7.** _____

For each statement below, write <u>true</u> or <u>false</u>.

_____ **8.** Much of what scientists know about australopithecines comes from the "Lucy"skeleton.

_____ **9.** "Lucy" is 3.5 billion years old.

_____ **10.** "Lucy" is classified as *A. africanus.*

_____ **11.** *A. afarensis* is the earliest known hominid species.

_____ **12.** *A. afarensis* walked on all four legs and had a humanlike brain.

_____ **13.** Australopithecines are alive today and can be found in southern Africa and Asia.

_____ **14.** Australopithecines probably played a role in the evolution of modern hominids.

Chapter 16 Primate Evolution, *continued*

Section 16.2 Human Ancestry

In your textbook, read about the emergence of modern humans.

Circle the letter of the choice that best completes the statement or answers the question.

15. The first skull of *Homo habilis* was discovered by
  a. Raymond Dart.
  b. Louis and Mary Leakey.
  c. Donald Johanson.
  d. Gert Terblance.

16. When compared to an australopithecine skull, the *Homo habilis* skull is
  a. more humanlike.
  b. less humanlike.
  c. more apelike.
  d. exactly the same.

17. Which of the following is *not* true about *Homo habilis?*
  a. They existed between 1.5 and 2 million years ago.
  b. They were the first hominids to make and use tools.
  c. They were probably scavengers of their food.
  d. They gave rise to *A. africanus.*

18. *Homo habilis* means
  a. "handy human."
  b. "tool-using human."
  c. "upright human."
  d. "talking human."

19. Of the primates below, which has the largest brain?
  a. *Homo habilis*
  b. *Homo erectus*
  c. an ape
  d. an australopithecine

20. Which of the following is *not* true about *Homo erectus?*
  a. They probably hunted.
  b. They were the first hominids to use fire.
  c. They may have given rise to hominids that resemble modern humans.
  d. They were found only in Africa.

21. *Homo sapiens* includes
  a. Neandertals.
  b. australopithecines.
  c. *A. africanus.*
  d. *A. afarensis.*

Determine whether each statement below best describes Neandertals, Cro-Magnons, or both.

_____ **22.** They lived in caves during the ice ages.

_____ **23.** They are identical to modern humans in height, skull, and teeth structure.

_____ **24.** They may have been the first hominids to develop religious views.

_____ **25.** They may have used language.

_____ **26.** They were talented toolmakers and artists.

Capítulo 16 La evolución de los primates

En tu libro de texto, lee sobre las características de los primates.

Completa la tabla indicando las estructuras y funciones que son características de los primates.

Estructura/Función	Primate
1. Cabeza redonda	
2. Cara aplanada	
3. Cabeza pequeña	
4. Tamaño relativamente grande del encéfalo	
5. Visión muy desarrollada	
6. Visión deficiente	
7. Visión binocular	
8. Capacidad de percibir colores	
9. No pueden percibir colores	
10. La visión es el sentido dominante	
11. El olfato es el sentido dominante	
12. Articulaciones inmóviles	
13. Articulaciones flexibles en los hombros	
14. Esqueleto adaptado para desplazarse entre los árboles	
15. Esqueleto adaptado para nadar	
16. Garras en manos y pies	
17. Uñas en manos y pies	
18. Ojos localizados en los lados de la cara	
19. Pies diseñados para agarrar objetos	
20. Pulgar oponible	

En tu libro de texto, lee sobre el origen de los primates.

Indica si cada enunciado es <u>verdadero</u> o <u>falso</u>.

_____ **21.** Los científicos creen que los primates aparecieron hace unos 66,000 años.

_____ **22.** Es probable que el primer primate haya sido un animal llamado *Purgatorius,* que parecía un estrepsirrino.

_____ **23.** Los antropoides son un grupo de primates de cuerpo pequeño.

_____ **24.** Los estrepsirrinos incluyen lémures y társidos.

_____ **25.** Los estrepsirrinos habitan los bosques pluviales tropicales de Suramérica.

Identifica los siguientes animales. Usa estas opciones: babuino, társido y mono araña. Después, en la segunda línea, escribe el grupo representado por cada animal. Usa estas opciones: mono del Nuevo Mundo, mono del Viejo Mundo y prosimio.

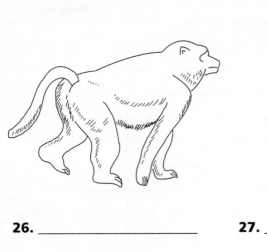  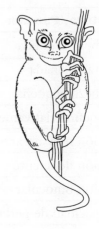

26. _____

_____

27. _____

_____

28. _____

_____

Contesta las siguientes preguntas.

29. ¿Qué sugieren las similitudes entre los monos, los simios y los humanos acerca de su evolución?

_____

_____

30. Según el registro fósil, ¿cuáles fueron los primeros antropoides modernos y aproximadamente cuándo aparecieron?

_____

_____

31. ¿En qué se basa la historia evolutiva de los primates?

_____

_____

32. ¿Qué factores produjeron la especiación de los babuinos y otros monos que viven en el suelo y no en los árboles?

_____

_____

33. ¿Qué sugiere el análisis del DNA de los homínidos modernos acerca de su historia evolutiva?

_____

_____

Capítulo 16 La evolución de los primates, *continuación*

Refuerzo y Guía de estudio

Sección 16.2 Los ancestros de los humanos

En tu libro de texto, lee acerca de los homínidos.

Contesta las siguientes preguntas.

1. ¿Qué es un australopiteco? _____

2. ¿Cuál cráneo fósil descubrió Raymond Dart en África, en 1924? _____

3. ¿Por qué el cráneo de *A. africanus* era diferente a los cráneos que Dart había estudiado antes? _____
_____

4. ¿Qué le indicó a Dart la posición del foramen magnum? _____
_____

Rotula los siguientes cráneos. Usa estas opciones: chimpancé, humano y *A. afarensis*

5. _____   **6.** _____   **7.** _____

Indica si cada enunciado es <u>verdadero</u> o <u>falso</u>.

_____ **8.** La mayoría del conocimiento que tienen los científicos acerca de los australopitecos proviene de los estudios del esqueleto de "Lucy".

_____ **9.** "Lucy" tiene una antigüedad de 3.5 billones de años.

_____ **10.** "Lucy" es clasificada como *A. africanus*.

_____ **11.** *A. afarensis* es la especie de homínidos más antigua que se conoce.

_____ **12.** *A. afarensis* caminó en cuatro patas y tenía un cerebro similar al cerebro humano.

_____ **13.** Los australopitecos todavía existen y habitan el sur de África y Asia.

_____ **14.** Probablemente, los australopitecos fueron importantes en la evolución de los homínidos modernos.

Capítulo 16 La evolución de los primates,
continuación

En tu libro de texto, lee sobre la aparición del ser humano moderno.

Marca la letra con la opción que complete mejor el enunciado o que conteste mejor la pregunta.

15. El primer cráneo de *Homo habilis* fue descubierto por
   a. Raymond Dart.
   b. Louis and Mary Leakey.
   c. Donald Johanson.
   d. Gert Terblance.

16. Si se compara con el cráneo de un australopiteco, el cráneo de *Homo habilis* es
   a. más semejante al humano.
   b. menos semejante al humano.
   c. más parecido a un simio.
   d. exactamente igual.

17. ¿Cuál de los siguientes enunciados *no* es verdadero acerca de *Homo habilis*?
   a. Existieron hace unos 1.5 y 2 millones de años.
   b. Fueron los primeros homínidos que fabricaron y usaron herramientas.
   c. Probablemente se alimentaron de carroña.
   d. Fueron los ancestros de *A. africanus*.

18. *Homo habilis* significa
   a. "hombre hábil".
   b. "hombre que usa herramientas".
   c. "hombre que camina erecto".
   d. "hombre que habla".

19. ¿Cuál de los siguientes primates tiene el cerebro más grande?
   a. *Homo habilis*
   b. *Homo erectus*
   c. un simio
   d. un australopiteco

20. ¿Cuál de los siguientes enunciados *no* es verdadero acerca de *Homo erectus*?
   a. Probablemente fueron cazadores.
   b. Fueron los primeros homínidos que usaron fuego.
   c. Quizás fueron los antepasados de homínidos semejantes al ser humano moderno.
   d. Habitaron sólo en África.

21. *Homo sapiens* incluye
   a. Neandertales.
   b. australopitecos.
   c. *A. africanus*.
   d. *A. afarensis*.

Determina si cada enunciado describe a neandertales, cromañones o ambos

_____ **22.** Vivieron en cavernas durante las glaciaciones.

_____ **23.** Son idénticos a los humanos modernos en estatura, cráneo y estructura de los dientes.

_____ **24.** Fueron quizás los primeros homínidos con pensamientos religiosos.

_____ **25.** Es probable que hayan desarrollado un lenguaje.

_____ **26.** Fueron hábiles fabricantes de herramientas y artistas.

Chapter 16   Primate Evolution

Use with Chapter 16, Section 16.1

Characteristics of Primates

Complete the concept map on the characteristics of primates. Use each of these words or phrases once: *grasping and clinging, memory, flexible joints, perception, mobility, face forward, large brain, hip, hands, distance, ball-and-socket structure, complex mental functions, opposable thumb, depth, use of tools, binocular vision, shoulder, eating.*

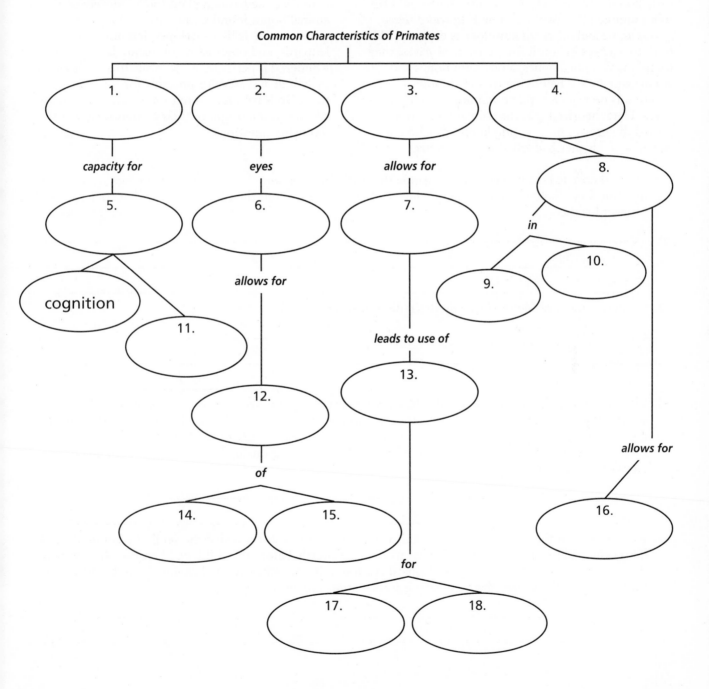

Interpreting the Fossil Record

Finding fossils of early hominids is just one part of the process of reconstructing human ancestry. Paleoanthropologists also infer information about the ecological niche and other aspects of the lives of early hominids. For several years after Raymond Dart first examined the fossil he named *Australopithecus africanus*, he and other paleontologists explored old limestone caves in South Africa. In these caves, they found many animal bones, along with bones and simple stone tools belonging to early hominids. There was no evidence that hominids lived in the caves. Dart theorized that the animal bones represented the prey of meat-eating hominids who consumed animals they had killed with weapons.

An Alternate Theory   Another paleontologist, Robert Brain, suspected that Dart's theory was not correct. The skulls of the hominid remains had large, heavily enameled teeth characteristic of animals that chew tough plant foods. Moreover, the animal bones found in the caves belonged not only to prey animals like antelopes, but also to hyenas, leopards, and other carnivorous predators. Brain wondered if perhaps animal predators, rather than early humans, were responsible for the bone collections. To learn more about these caves and the theories about the origin of their contents, answer the following questions.

1. Dart's theory led many scientists to assume that early humans were hunters who used weapons to kill animals for food. Suggest some types of additional information about the cave's contents that could be used to support his theory.

_____

_____

_____

2. Suggest some possible reasons why Brain did not accept Dart's theory.

_____

_____

_____

3. Brain observed that modern leopards often take their kills up into trees, where they consume them over several days. As the leopard eats, bones from its prey drop to the ground. Based on this observation, he developed the theory that ancient leopards fed in trees at the openings of the South African limestone caves. If this theory is correct, what does it imply about the relationship between early hominids and predators such as leopards?

_____

_____

4. Examination of the contents of a South African cave at Swartkrans revealed the skull of a hominid child. This skull had two puncture wounds that were made shortly before the child died because no healing of the wounds had taken place. A fossil leopard jaw found in the same cave had canine teeth that fit the puncture holes exactly. Which theory does this information support? Why?

_____

_____

Master
39 **Comparing Hands**

Use with Chapter 16, Section 16.1

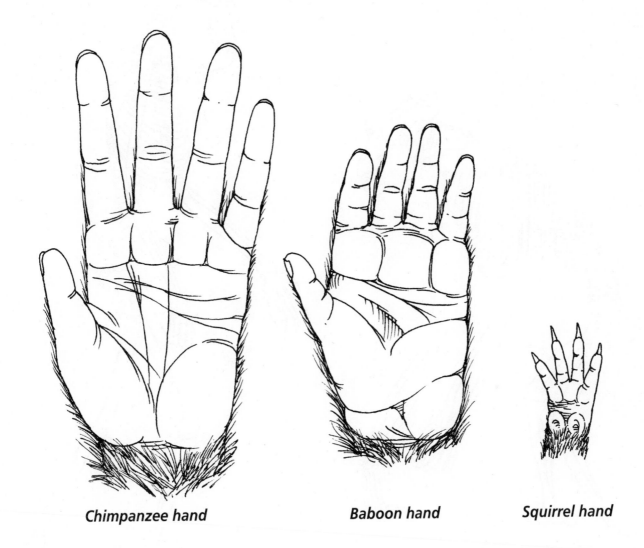

Chimpanzee hand   Baboon hand   Squirrel hand

❶ How are the chimpanzee hand and the baboon hand similar? How do
they differ from the squirrel hand?

❷ What tasks might a chimpanzee's hand enable the animal to complete
that the hand of the squirrel might not?

Master 40   Skeletal Clues

Use with Chapter 16, Section 16.2

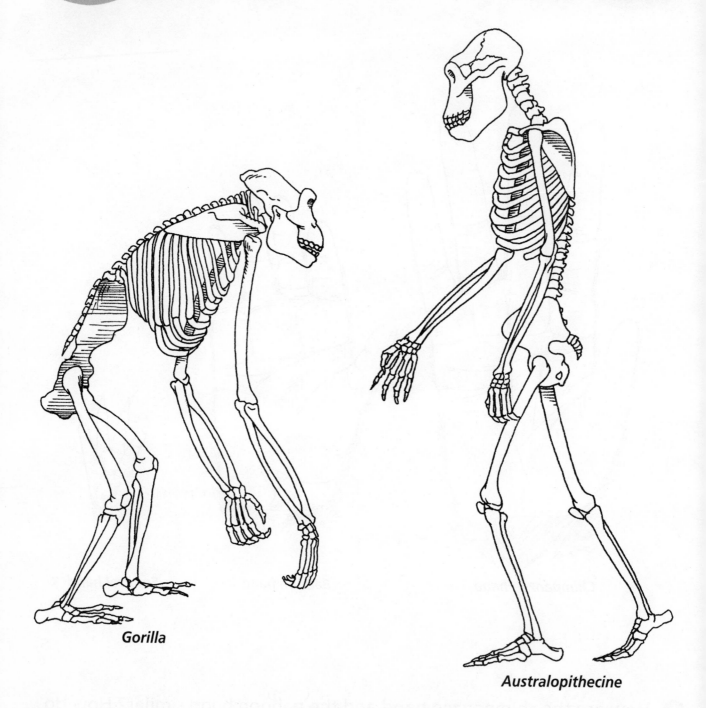

Gorilla

Australopithecine

❶ What do these skeletons suggest about the way each organism moved?

❷ How might the australopithecine be better suited than the gorilla for using tools?

Master 23

Possible Phylogeny of Humans

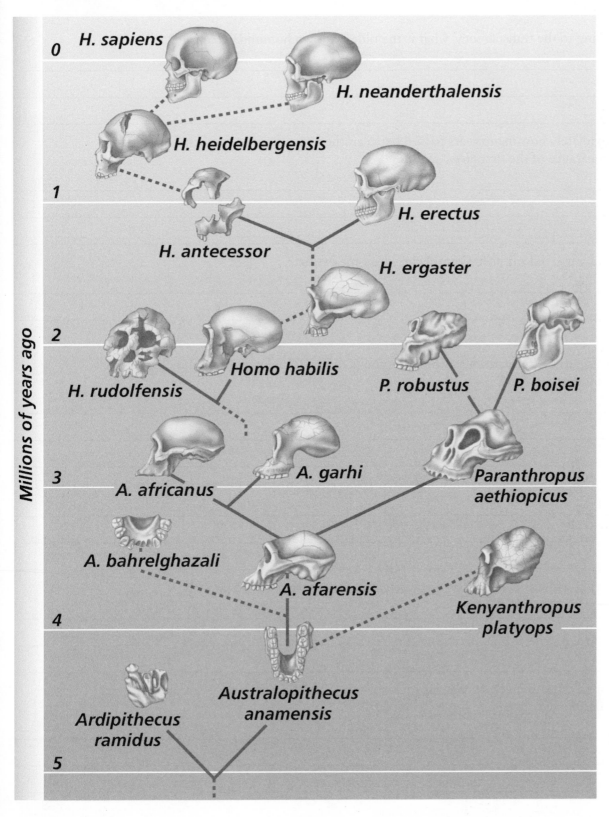

Millions of years ago

0 — H. sapiens
    H. neanderthalensis
    H. heidelbergensis

1 — H. antecessor
    H. erectus
    H. ergaster

2 — H. rudolfensis
    Homo habilis
    P. robustus
    P. boisei

3 — A. africanus
    A. garhi
    Paranthropus aethiopicus

    A. bahrelghazali
    A. afarensis
    Kenyanthropus platyops

4 — Australopithecus anamensis

    Ardipithecus ramidus

5 —

Possible Phylogeny of Humans

1. According to the transparency, what is the oldest known hominid? How old?

_____

_____

_____

2. Approximately how many years passed between the appearance of the first hominid and the appearance of the first *Homo sapiens*?

_____

_____

_____

3. How long ago did the australopithecines become extinct?

_____

_____

_____

4. According to the transparency, which hominids did *NOT* belong to the same branch that led to modern humans?

_____

_____

_____

5. What achievement may have distinguished *Homo erectus* from all preceding hominids?

_____

_____

_____

6. What view of Neandertals does the diagram in the transparency support?

_____

_____

_____

7. Apes are almost exclusively quadrupedal (they walk on all fours), while hominids are bipedal. Of what advantage is it to be bipedal?

_____

_____

_____

Master 25

Human Versus Primate Traits

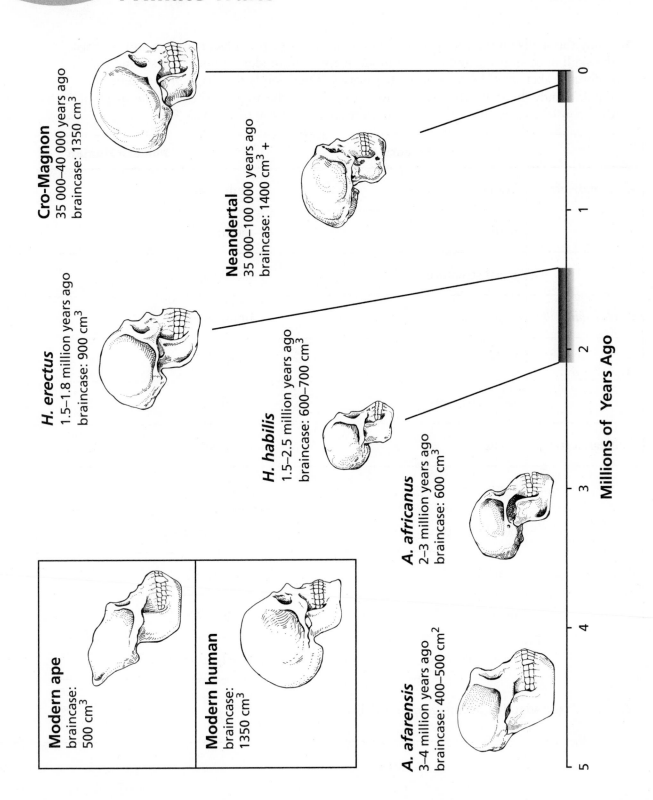

Cro-Magnon
35 000–40 000 years ago
braincase: 1350 cm^3

Neandertal
35 000–100 000 years ago
braincase: 1400 cm^3 +

H. erectus
1.5–1.8 million years ago
braincase: 900 cm^3

H. habilis
1.5–2.5 million years ago
braincase: 600–700 cm^3

A. africanus
2–3 million years ago
braincase: 600 cm^3

A. afarensis
3–4 million years ago
braincase: 400–500 cm^2

Modern ape
braincase: 500 cm^3

Modern human
braincase: 1350 cm^3

Millions of Years Ago

Human Versus Primate Traits

1. Study the skulls on the transparency. Then, in the space provided, compare and contrast the skull of each group and those of modern apes and modern humans. First, find the differences between the sizes of the braincases. Then, study the shape of the teeth. Finally, study the skulls themselves; note overall size, the angle of the face, the shape of the brow (the bone above the eyes), and the shape and size of the jaws.

	Modern Ape	**Modern Human**
a. *A. afarensis*	braincase:	braincase:
	teeth:	teeth:
	facial structure:	facial structure:
b. *H. habilis*	braincase:	braincase:
	teeth:	teeth:
	facial structure:	facial structure:
c. Neandertal	braincase:	braincase:
	teeth:	teeth:
	facial structure:	facial structure:
d. Cro-Magnon	braincase:	braincase:
	teeth:	teeth:
	facial structure:	facial structure:

2. What is the adaptive advantage of bipedalism?

_____

_____

Chapter 16 Primate Evolution

Reviewing Vocabulary

Complete the paragraphs by writing the correct term on the appropriate line. Use these choices:

haplorhines	bipedal	australopithecines	Neandertals	primates
hominids	prehensile tail	opposable thumb	Cro-Magnon	

A distinctive characteristic of humans is **(1)** _____ locomotion, the ability to

walk on two legs in an upright position. Another characteristic that humans share with most

(2) _____ is the ability to touch the thumb to the forefinger. Called the

(3) _____ , it permits objects to be tightly grasped.

Anthropologists are also concerned with the origin of humans. Primates are classified in two groups,

the strepsirrhines and the **(4)** _____ . The strepsirrhines are small-bodied and

include the lemurs and pottos. The other group can be divided into Old World monkeys, New World

monkeys, and hominoids. Hominoids include the humanlike, bipedal primates such as the apes, chim-

panzees, and gorillas. New World monkeys are entirely arboreal. Their success in the tree tops can be par-

tially attributed to their **(5)** _____ , which functions almost like an extra hand,

enabling them to tightly grasp branches.

Modern humans and humanlike fossils are classified as **(6)** _____ . Based on

fossil evidence and biochemical evidence, it is believed that apes and humans began to evolve about

30 million years ago, developing along different paths but arising from the same common ancestor. In

1924, Raymond Dart discovered a skull with both apelike and human characteristics. The skull derived

from the first of several African primates, now collectively referred to as **(7)** _____ ,

which show both humanlike and apelike qualities. *Homo sapiens* may have first appeared between 100 000

and 500 000 years ago. The first of the species to have communicated through spoken language appeared

around 100 000 years ago. They have been named **(8)** _____ . About 35 000 years

ago, these disappeared from the fossil record as a group called **(9)** _____ evolved.

Chapter 16 Primate Evolution, *continued*

Understanding Main Ideas (Part A)

In the space at the left, write the letter of the word or phrase that best completes the statement or answers the question.

_____ 1. Which is the oldest hominid species to be unearthed?
    a. *Homo habilis*   **b.** *Homo erectus*
    c. *Australopithecus afarensis*   **d.** *Australopithecus africanus*

_____ 2. The skeleton of the hominid nicknamed "Lucy" gave anthropologists evidence that
    a. cavemen coexisted with dinosaurs.
    b. Neandertals coexisted with *Homo habilis*.
    c. upright walking evolved after large brains.
    d. upright walking evolved before large brains.

_____ 3. Most early hominid fossils have been found in
    a. Egypt.   **b.** France.   **c.** Africa.   **d.** North America.

_____ 4. The earliest primate identifiable from the fossil record is
    a. *Purgatorius.*   **b.** *Australopithecus.*   **c.** *Neanderthalus.*   **d.** *Afarensis.*

_____ 5. The first hominids to make and use simple stone tools were
    a. *Homo sapiens.*   **b.** *Homo habilis.*
    c. *Australopithecus afarensis.*   **d.** *Australopithecus africanus.*

_____ 6. As primates evolved, they developed
    a. a good sense of smell and large lower vertebrae.
    b. good vision and large teeth.
    c. stereoscopic vision and rotating shoulder joints.
    d. large teeth and a well-developed collar bone.

_____ 7. The hominid that had the most advanced tool-making abilities and spoken language was
    a. Cro-Magnon.   **b.** Neandertal.   **c.** *Purgatorius.*   **d.** *Homo habilis.*

_____ 8. Based on the fossil record, it has been determined the earliest primates probably lived in the
    a. grasslands.   **b.** mountains.   **c.** forests.   **d.** deserts.

_____ 9. Primates evolved approximately
    a. 200 000 years ago.   **b.** 2 million years ago.
    c. 8 million years ago.   **d.** 66 million years ago.

_____ 10. The anthropologists who discovered the skull of *Homo habilis* were
    a. the Leakeys.   **b.** the Darts.   **c.** the Johansons.   **d.** the Priestleys.

Chapter 16 Primate Evolution, *continued*

Understanding Main Ideas (Part B)

In the space at the left, write the letter of the word or phrase that best completes the statement or answers the question.

_____ **1.** Which factor may have played a large role in human evolution?

a. a geologic event that released much radiation into the environment, which in time resulted in an increased mutation rate

b. climatic changes that caused existing primates to search for new food sources

c. flooding due to melting glaciers causing primates to seek refuge in the trees

d. massive grassland fires that caused existing primates to flee to the mountains

_____ **2.** Evidence that *Homo erectus* was more intelligent than its predecessors would include

a. a small cranial capacity as indicated by their skeletal remains.

b. involved messages they wrote on cave walls.

c. signs of agriculture and tilled fields.

d. tools, such as hand axes, that have been found near their fire pits.

_____ **3.** Some primate skeletons were located in a cave in association with these things: a variety of tools, the charred bones of some animals they had cooked and eaten, and numerous paintings on the walls. Carbon-14 dating techniques determined that the bones and other artifacts were about 35 000 years old. The skeletal remains probably belonged to

a. *A. afarensis.*　　　**b.** *Homo habilis.*　　　**c.** Cro-Magnons.　　　**d.** *Homo erectus.*

_____ **4.** The jaw from the skull of the genus *Homo* and one from the genus *Australopithecus* are different in that the jaw from the genus *Homo* would

a. be much heavier with large teeth and well-defined canines.

b. be smaller with smaller teeth and not so much definition of tooth type.

c. be larger with a multitude of small teeth with well-defined canines.

d. be smaller with larger teeth that were all about the same.

_____ **5.** The nucleotide sequence of human and chimpanzee genes differs by about only 1.6%. This fact, along with the fossil record, reveals that

a. humans descended from chimpanzees.

b. chimpanzees descended from humans.

c. humans and chimpanzees evolved from a common ancestor.

d. convergent evolution has resulted in chimpanzees and humans becoming more alike.

_____ **6.** Evidence for the determination of bipedal locomotion in an animal could be found by an examination of the

a. skull.　　　　　　　　　　**b.** upper arm (humerous).

c. finger (carpal).　　　　　**d.** jaw.

Thinking Critically

Answer the following questions.

1. Early primates spent most, if not all of their time in trees. How did their successful adaptations there eventually lead to important hominid adaptations?

_____

_____

_____

_____

_____

_____

_____

_____

_____

_____

2. Why is bipedal locomotion an important hominid trait?

_____

_____

_____

3. You are on an expedition searching for early hominid fossils. You unearth a jaw bone. What traits would indicate to you that you have discovered an ape jaw and not a hominid jaw?

_____

_____

_____

4. Why is it that we are still piecing together a picture of how human evolution occurred and how is it possible that our understanding of it might be flawed?

_____

_____

_____

_____

Chapter
16 **Primate Evolution,** *continued*

Applying Scientific Methods

It is speculated that environmental changes in the African habitat from warm, moist forest to cool, dry grassland exerted selection pressures on all native species, including prehumans. Of all the theories attempting to explain hominid evolution, the one presently receiving much attention links the emergence of humankind to wide-scale climatic change. Two such major events in human evolution occurred, the first 2.8 million years ago and the second, 1 million years ago.

Ocean-bottom core samples taken from the west coast of Africa, the Arabian Sea, and the Gulf of Aden off the east coast of Africa lend credibility to this theory. A thick layer of dust and silicate particles has been found in the cores at levels determined to have been deposited 2.8 million and 1 million years before the present. Scientists attribute the deposits to the fact that grasses draw large quantities of silicates from the soil and concentrate them in their tissues for structural use. In a grassland environment, as grasses live, die, and decompose over many years, quantities of silicates accumulate in the surface soil.

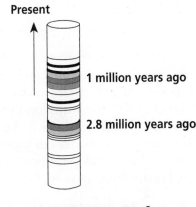

**Segment of
Ocean-Bottom Core**

Deposits of dust and silicates also coincide with ice sheet formation and the onset of two ice ages in the Northern Hemisphere. Computer models show that the cooling and ice sheet formation influenced weather in both hemispheres. The models illustrate how cool, dry winds would have been diverted toward Africa as the ice sheets grew.

Another important piece of information has been obtained from the Gulf of Aden core. It contains volcanic ash, along with dust and silicates blown by monsoon winds from the Rift Valley. This type of ash is also found in association with some hominid fossils discovered in the Rift Valley.

1. What does the above information tell us about the African environment that existed approximately 2.8 million and 1 million years ago? Explain.

_____

_____

_____

_____

2. Describe what the African environment might have been like 2 million years ago.

_____

_____

_____

_____

_____

_____

Chapter Assessment

Applying Scientific Methods   *continued*

3. In what way does the presence of volcanic ash in the Gulf of Aden cores and in the Rift Valley help in tracing human evolution?

_____

_____

_____

_____

When African forests declined and were replaced with vast areas of grassland, competition for food among animal species intensified. In an attempt to survive, hominids radiated outward from small forested areas. A vegetarian group, the australopithecines, emerged a few thousand years after the cooling period 2.8 million years ago. These hominids had to rely on seeds and tubers during the harsher seasons and on dense vegetation along river banks during the remainder of the year. Exploiting a variety of habitats at about the same time as the australopithecines was the first representative of the genus *Homo*. Members of this group consumed many kinds of food, including meat.

4. How would a diet of meat improve the chances of this group's survival, compared to australopithecines?

_____

_____

_____

_____

5. How would a diet of meat select for a different jaw and tooth structure than is seen in earlier primates?

_____

_____

_____

_____

_____

_____

_____

Chapter 16

Assessment
Student Recording Sheet

Vocabulary Review

If the statement is true, write *true*. If the statement is false, replace the underlined word with the correct vocabulary word.

1. _____
2. _____
3. _____
4. _____

Understanding Key Concepts

Select the best answer from the choices given and fill in the corresponding oval.

5. Ⓐ Ⓑ Ⓒ Ⓓ
6. Ⓐ Ⓑ Ⓒ Ⓓ
7. Ⓐ Ⓑ Ⓒ Ⓓ
8. Ⓐ Ⓑ Ⓒ Ⓓ
9. Ⓐ Ⓑ Ⓒ Ⓓ
10. Ⓐ Ⓑ Ⓒ Ⓓ

Constructed Response

Record your answers for Questions 11–13 on a separate sheet of paper.

Thinking Critically

14. **REAL WORLD BIOCHALLENGE** Follow your teacher's instructions for presenting your BioChallenge answer.

Record your answers for Questions 15–18 on a separate sheet of paper.

Standardized Test Practice

Part 1 Multiple Choice

Select the best answer from the choices given and fill in the corresponding oval.

19. Ⓐ Ⓑ Ⓒ Ⓓ
20. Ⓐ Ⓑ Ⓒ Ⓓ
21. Ⓐ Ⓑ Ⓒ Ⓓ

Part 2
Constructed Response/Grid In

Record your answers for Questions 22 and 23 on a separate sheet of paper.

Contents

Chapter 17 Organizing Life's Diversity

BioDigest 5 Change Through Time

Chapter 17

MiniLab 17.1

Classifying

Using a Dichotomous Key in a Field Investigation

How could you identify a tree growing in front of your school? You might ask a local expert, or you could use a manual or field guide that contains descriptive information or you might use a dichotomous key for trees. A key is a set of descriptive sentences that is subdivided into steps. A dichotomous key has two descriptions at each step. You follow the steps until the key reveals the name of the tree.

Procedure

1 Collect a few leaves from local trees and a dichotomous key for trees of your area, identify the tree from which each leaf came. To use the key, study one leaf. Then choose the one statement from the first pair that most accurately describes the leaf. Continue following the key until you identify the leaf's tree. Repeat the process for each leaf.

2 Glue each leaf on a separate sheet of paper. For each leaf, record the tree's name.

Analysis

1. What is the function of a dichotomous key?

_____

_____

2. List three different characteristics used in your key.

_____

_____

3. As you used the key, did the characteristics become more general or more specific?

_____

MiniLab 17.2

Classifying

Using a Cladogram to Show Relationships

Cladograms were developed by Willi Hennig. They use derived characteristics to illustrate evolutionary relationships.

Procedure

1 The following table shows the presence or absence of six derived traits in the seven dinosaurs that are labeled A–G.

2 Use the information listed in the table to answer the questions below.

Derived traits of dinosaurs							
Dinosaur trait	A	B	C	D	E	F	G
Hole in hip socket	yes	yes	yes	yes	yes	yes	yes
Extension of pubis bone	no	no	no	yes	yes	yes	yes
Unequal enamel on teeth	no	no	no	no	yes	yes	yes
Skull has "shelf" in back	no	no	no	no	no	yes	yes
Grasping hand	yes	yes	yes	no	no	no	no
Three-toed hind foot	yes	yes	no	no	no	no	no

Analysis

1. Copy the partially completed cladogram on page 453 of your text. Complete the missing information on the right side.

_____

2. How many traits does dinosaur F share with dinosaur C, with dinosaur D, and with dinosaur E?

_____

3. Dinosaurs A and B form a grouping called a clade. Dinosaurs A, B, and C form another clade. What derived trait is shared only by the A and B clade? By the A, B, and C clade? By the D, E, F, and G clade?

_____

_____

4. Traits that evolved early, such as the hole in the hip socket, are called primitive traits. Traits that evolved later, such as a grasping hand, are called derived traits. Are primitive traits typical of broader or smaller clades? Are derived traits typical of broader or smaller clades? Give an example in each case.

_____

_____

Making a Dichotomous Key

Chapter 17

Problem
How is a dichotomous key made?

Objectives
In this BioLab, you will:
- **Classify** organisms on the basis of structural characteristics.
- **Develop** a dichotomous key.

Materials
sample keys from guidebooks
metric ruler

Skill Handbook
Use the **Skill Handbook** if you need additional help with this lab.

1. Study the drawings of beetles on page 461 of your text.
2. Choose one characteristic of the beetles and classify the beetles into two groups based on that characteristic. Take measurements if you wish.
3. Record the chosen characteristic in a diagram like the one shown. Write the numbers of the beetles in each group on your diagram.
4. Continue to form subgroups within your two groups based on different characteristics.

Record the characteristics and numbers of the beetles in your diagram until you have only one beetle in each group.

5. Using the diagram you have just made, make a dichotomous key for the beetles. Remember that each numbered step should contain two choices for classification. Begin with 1A and 1B. For help, examine sample keys provided by your teacher.
6. Exchange dichotomous keys with another team. Use their keys to identify the beetles.

1. **Error Analysis** Was the dichotomous key you constructed exactly like those of the other students? Explain your answer.

_____

_____

_____

_____

_____

2. **Analyzing Data** What characteristics were most useful for making a classification key for beetles? What characteristics were not useful?

_____

_____

_____

_____

_____

3. **Thinking Critically** Why do keys typically offer only two choices and not more?

_____

_____

_____

_____

_____

Chapter
17 A Dichotomous Key

Many scientists use classification systems to identify organisms. An ornithologist (one who studies birds) may need to classify a certain type of bird found in a protected area. Or, a botanist studying pigments of plants may need to classify a certain type of plant based on its flower and other characteristics.

Classifying organisms is important in fields such as pest control (extermination) and commercial breeding. For example, a pest control technician is trained to learn about the different species of pests and ways to control them with chemicals. A technician may be responsible for identifying one of over 3000 species of cockroaches. To recognize each species, a technician may use a *dichotomous key*.

A dichotomous key consists of pairs of descriptions. By eliminating one of each pair of descriptions, scientists can narrow down the possibilities until one species has been identified.

Part A: How Can Organisms Be Classified?

1. The key shown below is part of a dichotomous key. Begin with the paired descriptions in 1a and 1b. Only one of the descriptions will apply to your organism. The number at the end of the description leads to the next pair of descriptions. If there is a name at the end of the description, it identifies your organism.

1a	Has 8 legs or fewer	2
1b	Has more than 8 legs	10
2a	Has 8 legs	3
2b	Has 6 legs or fewer	5
3a	Is brown	TRAP-DOOR SPIDER
3b	Is not brown	4

Using this partial key, list the order of descriptions you would use to identify a brown, 8-legged animal. Name the animal.

_____

_____

2. Now study the picture of the cockroach below.

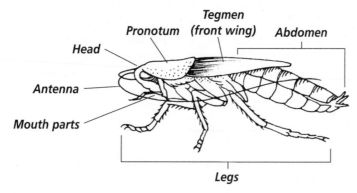

Figure 1

List some characteristics that you think you could use to describe a cockroach.

_____

_____

Chapter 17 **A Dichotomous Key**

Real World BioApplications

Part B: Classifying Cockroaches

In your science journal, create a key to classify the following 6 cockroaches (descriptions are of the male cockroach). Use the sample key in Part A as an example.

American Cockroach
• 27.8 to 34.2 mm
• pronotum is paler than front wings with base and central markings darker
• front wings are glossy reddish brown; front wings are longer than the abdomen
• front leg has many spines on underside plus one or more at the tip

German Cockroach
• 10.5 to 12.8 mm
• pale brownish-yellow; two dark brown stripes on pronotum
• front wings are reduced
• front leg has a row of spines that decrease gradually in size

Australian Cockroach
• 23 to 29 mm
• pronotum is yellowish at base with one or two large blackish-brown spots
• front wings are reddish-brown with yellow stripes in front at sides; front wings are longer than the abdomen
• front leg has a row of spines that decrease gradually in size

Little Gem Cockroach
• 7.5 to 9.7 mm
• glossy yellowish to brownish
• dark markings on abdomen and front wings
• front leg has a row of long spines followed by a row of short spines

Cuban Cockroach
• 12.2 to 18 mm
• pale green
• front wings often have a tiny brown spot about 1/3 from tip
• front leg has a few spines at the tip

Oriental Cockroach
• 18 to 24 mm
• shiny blackish brown
• front wings leave two or more segments of abdomen exposed
• front leg has many spines on underside plus one or more at the tip

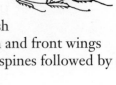

ANALYZE AND CONCLUDE

1. Why do you think a dichotomous key is more helpful than a book containing descriptions of organisms?

2. Do you think a dichotomous key could be created to classify nonliving items, such as rocks? Why or why not?

Chapter 17 Organizing Life's Diversity

Reinforcement and Study Guide

Section 17.1 Classification

In your textbook, read about how classification began and about biological classification.

For each item in Column A, write the letter of the matching item in Column B.

Column A	Column B
_____ **1.** Grouping objects or information based on similarities	**a.** Aristotle
_____ **2.** Naming system that gives each organism a two-word name	**b.** Linnaeus
_____ **3.** Developed the first system of classification	**c.** genus
_____ **4.** Branch of biology that groups and names organisms	**d.** classification
_____ **5.** Designed a system of classifying organisms based on their physical and structural similarities	**e.** taxonomy
_____ **6.** Consists of a group of similar species	**f.** binomial nomenclature

If the statement is true, write *true*. If it is not, rewrite the italicized part to make it true.

7. The scientific name of a species consists of a *family* name and a descriptive name.

_____

8. The scientific name of modern humans is *Homo sapiens*.

_____

9. *Latin* is the language of scientific names.

_____

10. The *scientific* names of organisms can be misleading.

_____

11. Taxonomists try to identify the *evolutionary relationships* among organisms.

_____

12. Besides comparing the structures of organisms, taxonomists also compare the organisms' geographic distribution and *chemical makeup*.

_____

13. Similarities between living species and extinct species *cannot* be used to determine their relationship to each other.

_____

14. Because the bones of some dinosaurs have large internal spaces, some scientists think dinosaurs are more closely related to *amphibians* than to reptiles.

_____

15. Classification can be useful in identifying the *characteristics* of an unknown organism.

_____

In your textbook, read about how living things are classified.

Examine the table showing the classification of four organisms. Then answer the questions.

Taxon	Green Frog	Mountain Lion	Domestic Dog	Human
Kingdom	Animalia	Animalia	Animalia	Animalia
Phylum	Chordata	Chordata	Chordata	Chordata
Class	Amphibia	Mammalia	Mammalia	Mammalia
Order	Anura	Carnivora	Carnivora	Primates
Family	Ranidae	Felidae	Canidae	Hominidae
Genus	*Rana*	*Felis*	*Canis*	*Homo*
Species	*Rana clamitans*	*Felis concolor*	*Canis familiaris*	*Homo sapiens*

16. Which taxon includes the most specific characteristics? _____

17. Which taxon includes the broadest characteristics? _____

18. Which taxon includes more species, an order or a family? _____

19. Which taxon includes only organisms that can successfully interbreed? _____

20. If two organisms belong to the same family, what other taxonomic groups do the organisms have in common.

_____

21. Which two organisms in the chart are most closely related? Explain.

_____

_____

_____

22. To which taxa do all four organisms belong?

_____

23. Which class does not include animals that have hair or fur? _____

24. What is the order, family, and genus of a human?

_____

25. Using the information in the chart, what can you conclude about the classification taxa of an organism with the scientific name *Rana temporaria*?

_____

_____

_____

Chapter 17 Organizing LIfe's Diversity, continued

Reinforcement and Study Guide

Section 17.2 The Six Kingdoms

In your textbook, read about how evolutionary relationships are determined.

Explain how scientists use each item below to determine the evolutionary relationships among organisms.

1. structural similarities: _____

_____

2. breeding behavior: _____

_____

3. geographical distribution: _____

_____

4. chromosome comparisons: _____

_____

5. biochemistry: _____

_____

In your textbook, read about phylogenetic classification: models.

Use the cladogram to answer the questions.

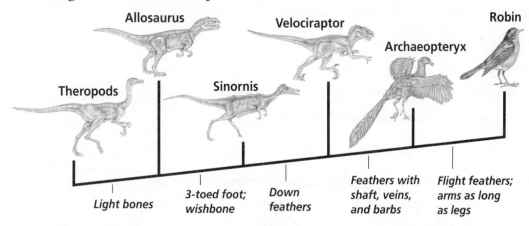

6. What five probable ancestors of the modern bird (robin) are shown on the cladogram?

_____

7. Which dinosaur is probably the most recent common ancestor of *Velociraptor* and *Archaeopteryx*?

_____

8. Which traits shown on the cladogram are shared by *Archaeopteryx* and modern birds?

_____

_____

Use the fanlike phylogenetic diagram to answer the questions.

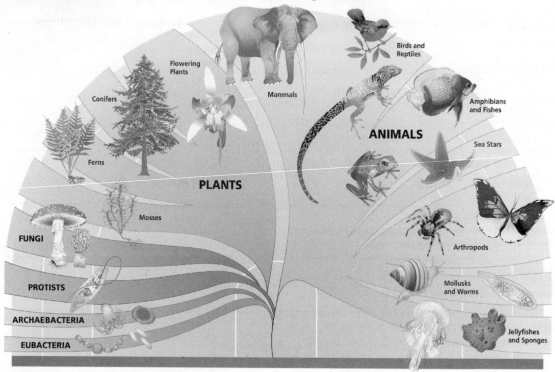

9. How does the fanlike diagram differ from a cladogram?

_____

_____

10. To which group are sea stars more closely related, arthropods or jellyfishes? _____

11. Which group of animals includes the fewest species? _____

In your textbook, read about the six kingdoms of organisms.

Circle the letter of the choice that best completes the statement or answers the question.

12. Organisms that do not have a nucleus bounded by a membrane are
    a. multicellular.   **b.** eukaryotes.   **c.** protists.   **d.** prokaryotes.

13. Fungi obtain food by
    a. photosynthesis.   **b.** chemosynthesis.
    c. endocytosis.   **d.** absorbing nutrients from organic materials.

14. Animals are
    a. autotrophs.   **b.** heterotrophs.   **c.** prokaryotes.   **d.** stationary.

Capítulo 17 Organización de la diversidad de la vida

Sección 17.1 Clasificación

En tu libro de texto, lee sobre cómo empezó la clasificación y sobre la clasificación biológica.

Escribe la letra de la columna B que corresponde a cada enunciado de la columna A.

Columna A	Columna B
_____ 1. Agrupación de objetos o información según sus similitudes	**a.** Aristóteles
_____ 2. Sistema que nombra cada organismo usando dos palabras	**b.** Linneo
_____ 3. Desarrolló el primer sistema de clasificación	**c.** género
_____ 4. Rama de la biología que clasifica y nombra los organismos	**d.** clasificación
_____ 5. Diseñó un sistema de clasificación de los organismos con base en sus similitudes físicas y estructurales	**e.** taxonomía
_____ 6. Consta de un grupo de especies similares	**f.** nomenclatura binaria

Si el enunciado es verdadero, escribe *verdadero*; de lo contrario, modifica la sección en itálicas para hacer verdadero el enunciado.

7. El nombre científico de una especie consta del nombre de la *familia* y un nombre descriptivo.

_____

8. El nombre científico del humano moderno es *Homo sapiens*.

_____

9. La lengua que se usa para los nombres científicos es el *latín*.

_____

10. Los nombres *científicos* de los organismos pueden ser confusos.

_____

11. Los taxónomos tratan de determinar las *relaciones evolutivas* entre los organismos.

_____

12. Además de comparar las estructuras de los organismos, los taxónomos también comparan su distribución geográfica y su *composición química*.

_____

13. Las similitudes entre las especies vivas y las especies extintas *no se pueden* usar para determinar su relación.

_____

14. Debido a que los huesos de algunos dinosaurios tienen grandes espacios internos, algunos científicos creen que los dinosaurios están más estrechamente relacionados con *los anfibios* que con los reptiles.

_____

15. La clasificación puede servir para identificar las *características* de un organismo desconocido.

_____

Capítulo
17 **Organización de la diversidad**
de la vida, *continuación*

En tu libro de texto, lee sobre cómo se clasifican los animales.

Examina la tabla que muestra la clasificación de cuatro organismos y contesta las preguntas

Taxón	Rana verde	Puma	Perro doméstico	Humano
Reino	Animalia	Animalia	Animalia	Animalia
Filo	Chordata	Chordata	Chordata	Chordata
Clase	Amphibia	Mammalia	Mammalia	Mammalia
Orden	Anura	Carnivora	Carnivora	Primates
Familia	Ranidae	Felidae	Canidae	Hominidae
Género	*Rana*	*Felis*	*Canis*	*Homo*
Especie	*Rana clamitans*	*Felis concolor*	*Canis familiaris*	*Homo sapiens*

16. ¿Cuál taxón incluye las características más específicas? _____

17. ¿Cuál taxón incluye las características más generales? _____

18. ¿Cuál taxón incluye más especies: el orden o la familia? _____

19. ¿Cuál taxón incluye sólo organismos que se pueden cruzar entre sí y generar progenie fértil? _____

20. Si dos organismos pertenecen a la misma familia, ¿qué otras categorías taxonómicas tienen en común.

_____

21. ¿Cuáles son los dos organismos de la tabla que están relacionados más estrechamente? Explica.

_____

_____

_____

_____

22. ¿Cuáles taxones tienen en común los cuatro organismos?

_____

23. ¿Cuál clase no incluye animales que tienen pelo o piel? _____

24. ¿Cuál es el orden, la familia y el género de los humanos?

_____

25. De acuerdo con la información de la tabla, ¿cuáles serían los taxones a los que pertenecería un organismo cuyo nombre científico fuera *Rana temporaria?*

_____

_____

_____

Refuerzo y Guía de estudio

Sección 17.2 Los seis reinos

En tu libro de texto, lee sobre cómo se determinan las relaciones evolutivas.

Explica cómo usan los científicos los siguientes factores para determinar las relaciones evolutivas entre organismos.

1. similitudes estructurales: _____

_____

2. comportamiento reproductor: _____

_____

3. distribución geográfica: _____

_____

4. comparación de los cromosomas: _____

_____

5. bioquímica: _____

_____

En tu libro de texto, lee sobre los modelos de clasificación filogenética.

Usa el cladograma para contestar las preguntas.

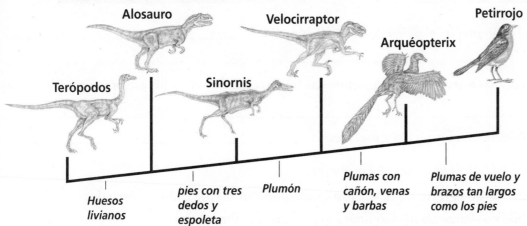

6. ¿Cuáles son los cinco probables antepasados del petirrojo moderno que se muestran en el cladograma?

_____

7. ¿Cuál dinosaurio es probablemente el antepasado común más reciente de *Velocirraptor* y *Arquéopterix*?

_____

8. De acuerdo con el cladograma, ¿cuál rasgo comparten las aves modernas y *Arquéopterix*?

_____

_____

Organización de la diversidad de la vida, *continuación*

Usa el diagrama filogenético para contestar las siguientes preguntas.

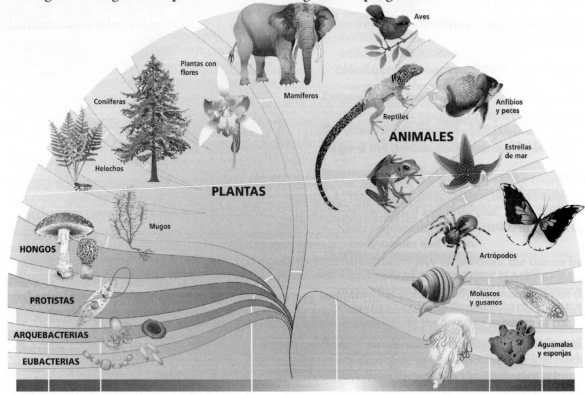

9. ¿En que difiere el diagrama de abanico de un cladograma? _____

_____

10. ¿A cuál grupo están más estrechamente relacionadas las estrellas de mar: a los artrópodos o a las agua-

malas? _____

11. ¿Cuál grupo de animales incluye menos especies? _____

En tu libro de texto, lee sobre los seis reinos de organismos.

Haz un círculo alrededor de la letra de la opción que completa mejor cada enunciado.

12. Los organismos que no tienen un núcleo limitado por una membrana son
    a. multicelulares.   **b.** eucariotas.   **c.** protistas.   **d.** procariotas.

13. Los hongos obtienen su alimento mediante
    a. fotosíntesis.   **b.** quimiosíntesis.
    c. endocitosis.   **d.** absorción de nutrientes de la materia orgánica.

14. Los animales son
    a. autótrofos.   **b.** heterótrofos.   **c.** procariotas.   **d.** estacionarios.

Chapter 17 Organizing Life's Diversity

Use with Chapter 17, Sections 17.1, 17.2

Classifying Organisms

Make a concept map identifying the six kingdoms into which organisms are classified. Show whether the organisms in each kingdom are prokaryotes or eukaryotes; unicellular or multicellular; autotrophs or heterotrophs.

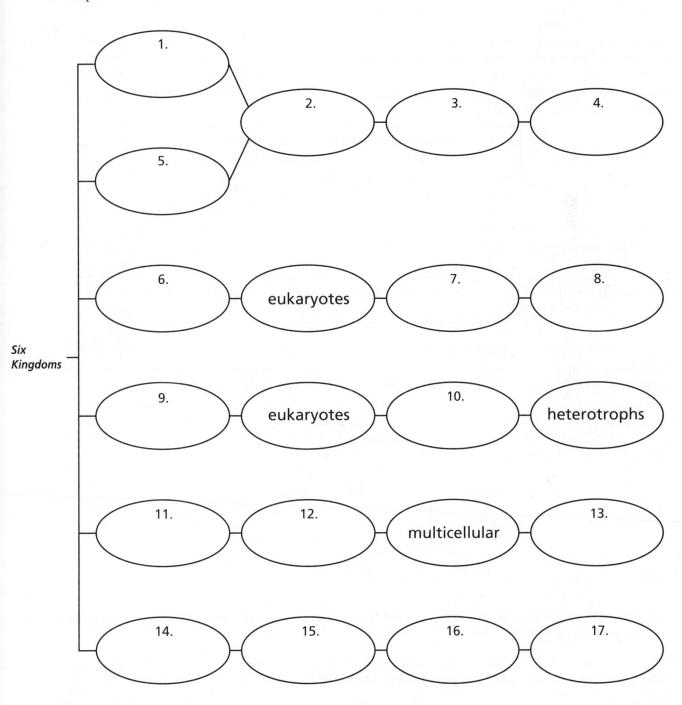

Six Kingdoms

Chapter 17 Organizing Life's Diversity

Evaluating Methods of Classification

Until recently, in order to classify living things, scientists compared the body parts of organisms or examined their tissues under a microscope. They also had the fossil record, but much of it was incomplete. Today, classification systems can be checked and revised by looking at the biochemistry of organisms and comparing the structures of their DNA and their proteins.

Amino-Acid Sequences In the 1970s, scientists Walter Fitch and Emanuel Margoliash revealed detailed comparisons of the amino-acid sequences of a protein called cytochrome c from different species. This protein exists in slightly different forms, yet it performs a similar function of energy transport in hundreds of different species. Fitch and Margoliash worked on the assumption that the more closely the sequences resembled each other, the more closely the species were related. The table below shows some of the sequences they found for cytochrome c.

Amino-Acid Sequences 1–25 for Cytochrome c
Tuna   GDVAKGKKTFVQKCAQCHTVENGGK
Moth   GNADNGKKIFVQRCAQCHTVEAGGK
Dog   CDVEKGKKIFVQKCAQCHTVEKGGK
Wheat GNPDAGAKIFKTKCAQCHTVDAGAG

1. Which two organisms shown on the table are the most closely related? Explain your answer.

_____

2. Should a moth be classified as being more similar to a tuna or more similar to wheat? Explain.

_____

_____

Based on their analysis of the differences in sequences of cytochrome c, Fitch and Margoliash drew a phylogenetic diagram. Part of a similar diagram is shown in the figure below.

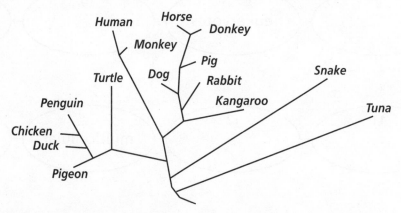

3. Older systems of classification always placed birds in their own group and turtles and snakes in the reptile group. Does the diagram support this? Explain.

_____

4. According to this diagram, are humans more closely related to the kangaroo or the tuna?

_____

Master 41 **Classification**

Use with Chapter 17, Section 17.1

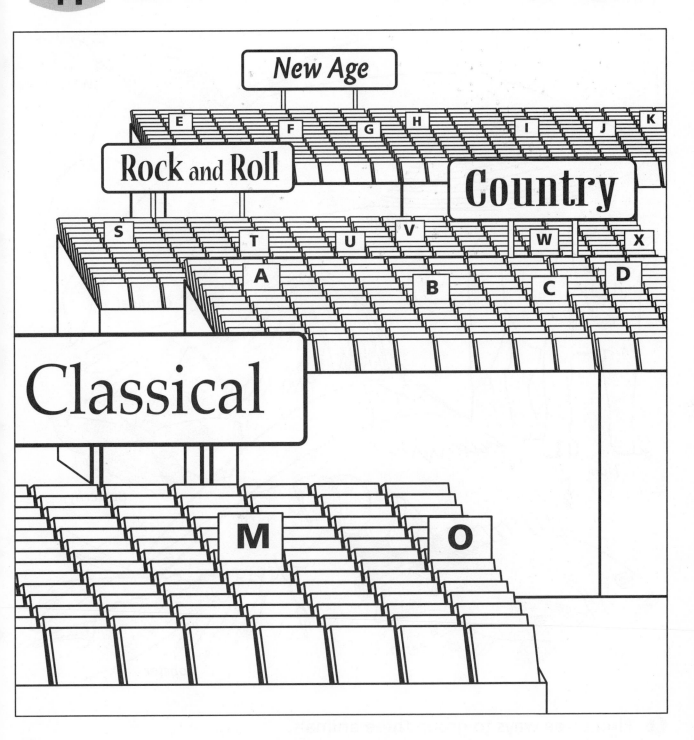

1 How is the music grouped in this store?

2 What is an advantage of grouping music this way?

Master
42 **Classifying Organisms**

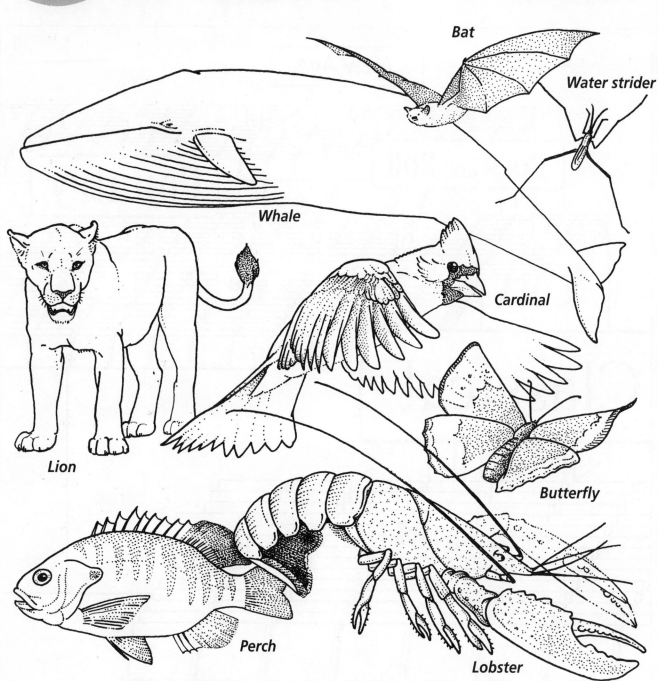

Bat

Water strider

Whale

Cardinal

Lion

Butterfly

Perch

Lobster

1 Find three ways to group these animals.

2 What characteristics did you use for each of your classifications?

Master 24 Life's Six Kingdoms

Use with Chapter 17, Section 17.2

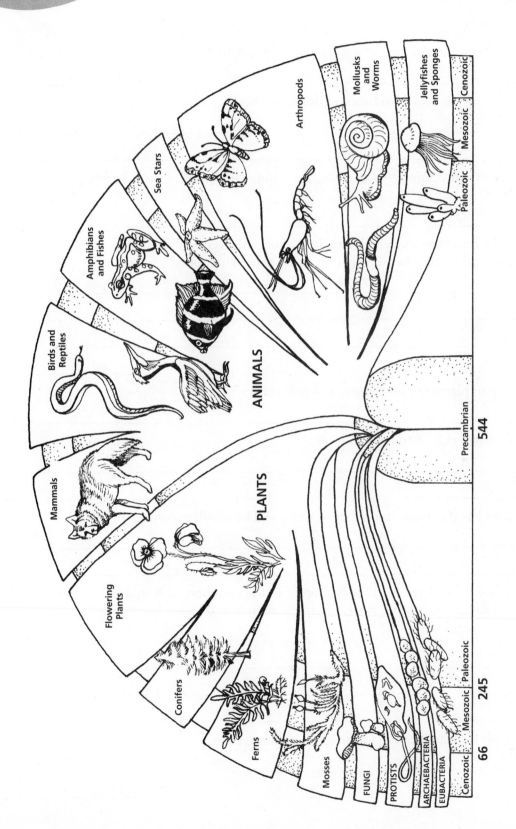

Mollusks and Worms

Jellyfishes and Sponges

Arthropods

Sea Stars

Amphibians and Fishes

Birds and Reptiles

ANIMALS

Mammals

Flowering Plants

PLANTS

Conifers

Ferns

Mosses

FUNGI

PROTISTS

ARCHAEBACTERIA

EUBACTERIA

Cenozoic

Mesozoic

Paleozoic

Precambrian

544

245

66

Cenozoic

Mesozoic

Paleozoic

Eras: shown in millions of years

Worksheet
24 Life's Six Kingdoms

Use with Chapter 17, Section 17.2

1. Based on the transparency, which of the six kingdoms evolved first?

_____

2. Which group of animals evolved most recently? About how long ago did this group evolve?

_____

_____

3. If organisms evolve increasing structural organization, which are the most highly organized plants?

_____

4. According to the transparency, which kingdom of organisms might be the common ancestor of three other kingdoms? What are those three kingdoms?

_____

_____

_____

_____

5. To which group of plants are mosses most closely related?

_____

6. What was the first group of animals to evolve?

_____

_____

7. Which kingdom has the greatest number of species? The smallest number of species?

_____

_____

8. What is the cellular characteristic that distinguishes the members of Kingdom Eubacteria and Kingdom Archaebacteria from the members of the other four kingdoms?

_____

_____

_____

_____

9. What is the basis for classification in the six-kingdom system?

_____

_____

Master 26 **Six Kingdoms**

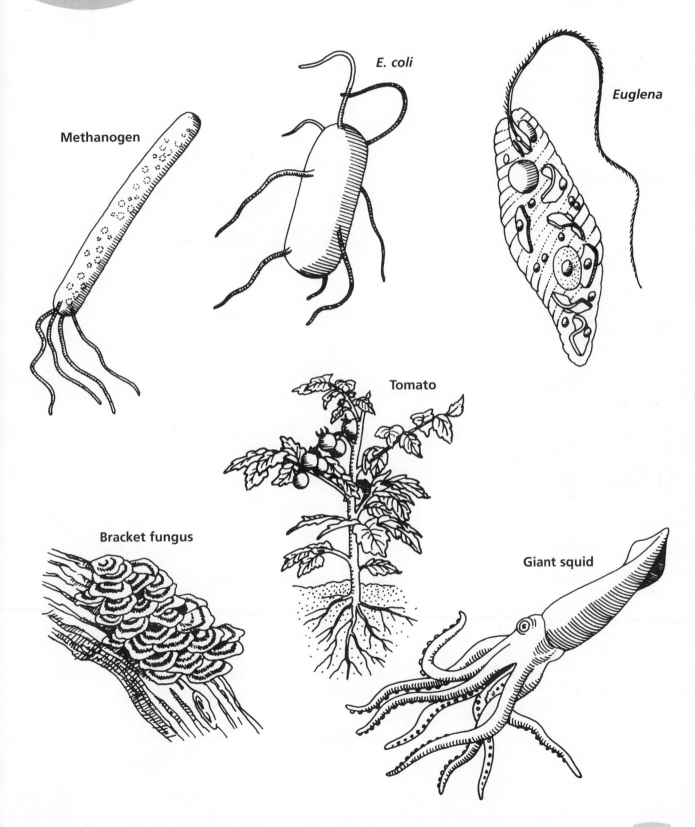

Methanogen

E. coli

Euglena

Tomato

Bracket fungus

Giant squid

Worksheet
26 **Six Kingdoms**

1. Study the representatives of each of the six kingdoms. Fill in the chart below, listing distinctive characteristics of the members of each kingdom.

a.	Eubacteria	
b.	Archaebacteria	
c.	Protists	
d.	Fungi	
e.	Plants	
f.	Animals	

2. What broad characteristics do biologists use to group living things into kingdoms?

_____

_____

3. Not too long ago, archaebacteria and eubacteria belonged to the same kingdom, Kingdom Monera. Their appearance is similar—both have similar shapes, are unicellular, and have no membrane-bound nucleus. Explain why biologists may have decided to divide the kingdom in two.

_____

_____

_____

Chapter 17 Organizing Life's Diversity

Reviewing Vocabulary

Match the definition in Column A with the term in Column B.

Column A	Column B
_____ **1.** Group of related phyla	**a.** class
_____ **2.** Classification system based on phylogeny	**b.** family
_____ **3.** Group of related orders	**c.** genus
_____ **4.** Evolutionary history of a species	**d.** kingdom
_____ **5.** Group of related genera	**e.** cladistics
_____ **6.** Group of related species	**f.** order
_____ **7.** Group of related classes	**g.** phylum
_____ **8.** Group of related families	**h.** phylogeny

In the space at the left, write the letter of the word or phrase that _____ ment.

_____ **9.** The branch of biology that group

    a. classification.   **b.** phyloge

_____ **10.** A group of related classes of plant

    a. order.   **b.** kingdom

_____ **11.** A heterotrophic eukaryote that ab   vi-
ronment is a(n)

    a. bacterium.   **b.** herbivore.

_____ **12.** The placing of information or obje

    a. biochemical analysis.

    c. phylogeny.

_____ **13.** The system for identifying organism

    a. binomial nomenclature.   **b.** dichotomous keying.

    c. cladistics.   **d.** fan diagramming.

_____ **14.** Prokaryotes that live in most habitats are

    a. protists.   **b.** eubacteria.   **c.** archaebacteria.   **d.** fungi.

Chapter 17   **Organizing Life's Diversity,** *continued*

Chapter Assessment

Understanding Main Ideas (Part A)

In the space at the left, write <u>true</u> if the statement is true. If the statement is false, change the italicized word or phrase to make the statement true.

_____ **1.** In Aristotle's system of classification, animals were classified on the basis of their *size and structure.*

_____ **2.** The greater the number of taxa two organisms have in common, the *more closely* related they are.

_____ **3.** Organisms that are similar in structure and form and successfully interbreed belong to the same *family.*

_____ **4.** A phylum is related to a class as a family is related to *an order.*

_____ **5.** In the scientific name of the white oak, *Quercus alba, Quercus* is the *species* name.

_____ **6.** Two groups of organisms that are farther from each other on a cladogram share *more* derived traits than groups that are closer to each other.

_____ **7.** In a fanlike diagram, groups represented by rays that begin *closer to* the edge of the fan evolved more recently.

_____ **8.** When organisms are classified within the same group, it can be assumed that they have a common *phylogeny.*

_____ **9.** *Escherichia coli,* a type of bacterium that lives in the small intestine, is classified in the Kingdom *Protista.*

_____ **10.** Linnaeus used similarities in *structure* to determine relationships among organisms.

Classify each of the following as a bacterium, protist, or fungus.

11.   **12.**   **13.**

_____   _____   _____

Understanding Main Ideas (Part B)

Answer the following questions.

1. What was one shortcoming of Aristotle's classification system?

_____

_____

2. What are two advantages of using scientific names for organisms?

_____

_____

_____

_____

_____

3. On what basis are members of one kingdom distinguished from those of another kingdom?

_____

_____

Complete the following table of the characteristics of the six kingdoms.

	Characteristic	Eubacteria and Archaebacteria	Protista	Fungi	Plantae	Animalia
4.	Cell type	a.	b.	c.	d.	eukaryotic
5.	Body form	a.	b.	c.	multicellular	d.
6.	Method of obtaining food	heterotrophic or autotrophic	a.	b.	c.	d.
7.	Presence of complex organ systems	a.	b.	no	c.	d.

Thinking Critically

The table below shows the complete classification of several species of animals. Use the table to answer the questions that follow.

Organism	House cat	Red Fox	Dog	Wolf	Gopher	Fly
Kingdom	Animalia	Animalia	Animalia	Animalia	Animalia	Animalia
Phylum	Chordata	Chordata	Chordata	Chordata	Chordata	Arthropoda
Class	Mammalia	Mammalia	Mammalia	Mammalia	Mammalia	Insecta
Order	Carnivora	Carnivora	Carnivora	Carnivora	Rodentia	Diptera
Family	Felidae	Canidae	Canidae	Canidae	Geomyidae	Muscidae
Genus	*Felis*	*Vulpes*	*Canis*	*Canis*	*Thomomys*	*Musca*
Species	*F. domesticus*	*V. fulva*	*C. familiaris*	*C. lupus*	*T. bottae*	*M. domestica*

1. What kind of animal is *Vulpes velox*? How do you know?

_____

_____

2. What is the complete classification of *Vulpes velox*?

_____

_____

_____

3. From the table, which two animals are most closely related? Explain.

_____

_____

_____

4. At what classification level does the evolutionary relationship between gophers and house cats diverge?

_____

_____

5. How does the table indicate that a dog is more closely related to a red fox than to a house cat?

_____

_____

Chapter 17 **Organizing Life's Diversity,** *continued*

Applying Scientific Methods

When a sample solution of DNA is heated to about 80°C, the DNA "melts," separating into single strands of nucleotides. If the sample is then cooled slightly and incubated, matching nucleotide sequences begin to reassociate. The solution can then be filtered to allow the single strands to pass through.

One technique for comparing DNA of different species involves the labeling of single strands of DNA with radioactive iodine and using the labeled DNA to form hybrid DNA. In this procedure, a small amount of labeled, single-stranded DNA from one species is mixed with a large amount of unlabeled, single-stranded DNA from another species and the mixture is incubated over time. A percentage of the strands form hybrid DNA consisting of one labeled and one unlabeled strand. (See Figure 1.)

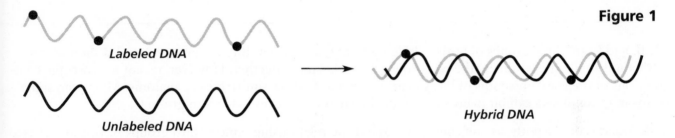

Figure 1

Labeled DNA

Unlabeled DNA

Hybrid DNA

The more closely related the two species are, the greater the number of matched sequences there will be in the hybrid DNA. (See Figure 2.) Hybrid DNA with a high proportion of matched sequences melts at higher temperatures than that with a low proportion of matched sequences.

Regions of matched sequences

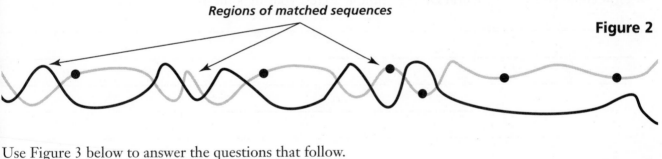

Figure 2

Use Figure 3 below to answer the questions that follow.

Figure 3

Hybrid A

Hybrid B

1. Which hybrid DNA was formed by DNA from two closely related species?

_____

2. Which hybrid DNA would melt at a lower temperature when heated?

_____

Chapter
17 Organizing Life's Diversity, continued

Applying Scientific Methods   continued

3. A solution containing Hybrid A is heated in stages, in 2.5-degree increments, from 55°C to 95°C and filtered at each stage to let single strands of DNA pass through. The radioactivity of the filtered material is measured at each stage. Would you expect to find a higher radioactivity level at 60°C or 85°C? Why?

_____

_____

_____

_____

A, B, and C are three groups of birds belonging to the same order. Birds in groups A and B show some structural similarities. Initially the two groups were classified together. However, recent microscopic comparisons of the vocal apparatus of birds in groups A and C show similarities in anatomy. Moreover, some birds in group A also exhibit many of the same behavioral patterns as birds in group C.

4. What is one hypothesis you could form about the relationships among bird groups A, B, and C, based on the given information?

_____

_____

5. How could you use the hybrid DNA technique to test your hypothesis?

_____

_____

_____

_____

_____

6. What would be the independent and dependent variables in your experiment?

_____

_____

_____

7. What control could you devise?

_____

_____

Chapter 17 Assessment
Student Recording Sheet

Vocabulary Review

Write the vocabulary words that match the definitions in your book.

1. _____   4. _____

2. _____   5. _____

3. _____

Understanding Key Concepts

Select the best answer from the choices given and fill in the corresponding oval.

6. Ⓐ Ⓑ Ⓒ Ⓓ   9. Ⓐ Ⓑ Ⓒ Ⓓ

7. Ⓐ Ⓑ Ⓒ Ⓓ   10. Ⓐ Ⓑ Ⓒ Ⓓ

8. Ⓐ Ⓑ Ⓒ Ⓓ   11. Ⓐ Ⓑ Ⓒ Ⓓ

Constructed Response

Record your answers for Questions 12–14 on a separate sheet of paper.

Thinking Critically

Record your answer for Question 15 on a separate sheet of paper.

16.   Fill in the correct terms to complete the concept map.

1. _____   4. _____

2. _____   5. _____

3. _____

17.   **REAL WORLD BIOCHALLENGE** Follow your teacher's instructions for presenting your BioChallenge answer.

Standardized Test Practice

The Princeton Review

Part 1   Multiple Choice

Select the best answer from the choices given and fill in the corresponding oval.

18. Ⓐ Ⓑ Ⓒ Ⓓ   21. Ⓐ Ⓑ Ⓒ Ⓓ

19. Ⓐ Ⓑ Ⓒ Ⓓ   22. Ⓐ Ⓑ Ⓒ Ⓓ

20. Ⓐ Ⓑ Ⓒ Ⓓ   23. Ⓐ Ⓑ Ⓒ Ⓓ

Part 2
Constructed Response/Grid In

Record your answers for Questions 24 and 25 on a separate sheet of paper.

BioDigest

5 Change Through Time

In your textbook, read about the geologic time scale.

Complete the table.

Era	Time period	Biologic event
1.	4.6 billion–600 million years ago	**2.**
3.	600 million–248 million years ago	**4.**
5.	248 million–65 million years ago	**6.**
7.	65 million years ago–present	**8.**

In your textbook, read about origin of life theories.

Complete each statement.

 9. Spontaneous generation assumes that life arises spontaneously from _____ .

10. Francesco Redi and Louis Pasteur designed _____ to disprove spontaneous generation.

11. The theory of _____ states that life comes only from pre-existing life.

12. Clusters of organic molecules might have formed _____ , which may have evolved into the first true cells.

Order the evolutionary development of the following organisms from 1 to 4.

_____ **13.** chemosynthetic prokaryotes   _____ **15.** heterotrophic prokaryotes

_____ **14.** eukaryotes   _____ **16.** oxygen-producing photosyn- thetic prokaryotes

In your textbook, read about the evidence and mechanics of evolution.

Answer the following questions.

17. What assumption is made in the relative dating of fossils? _____

_____

18. What are homologous structures? _____

_____

For each statement below, write true or false.

_____ **19.** Evolution occurs when a population's genetic equilibrium remains unchanged.

_____ **20.** Mutations, genetic drift, and migration may disrupt the genetic equilibrium of populations.

_____ **21.** Stabilizing selection favors the survival of a population's average individuals for a feature.

_____ **22.** Disruptive selection occurs when an extreme feature is naturally selected.

_____ **23.** Adaptive radiation occurs when species that once were similar to an ancestral species become increasingly distinct due to natural selection pressures.

In your textbook, read about primate evolution.

For each item in Column A, write the letter of the matching item in Column B.

Column A	Column B
_____ **24.** Primate adaptation	**a.** anthropoids
_____ **25.** Primate category that includes humans and apes	**b.** Australopithecines
_____ **26.** Characteristic of New World monkeys	**c.** genus *Homo*
_____ **27.** Appearing in fossil record about 2 million years ago along with stone tools	**d.** opposable thumb
_____ **28.** Possible human ancestors dating from 5 to 8 million years ago	**e.** prehensile tail

In your textbook, read about organizing life's diversity.

Look at the taxonomic classification of a bobcat shown below. Answer the questions.

29. What is the largest taxon in this classification system?

_____

30. What is the scientific name of a bobcat?

_____

Taxon	Name
Kingdom	*Animalia*
Phylum	*Chordata*
Class	*Mammalia*
Order	*Carnivora*
Family	*Felidae*
Genus	*Lynx*
Species	*rufus*

5 Cambios a través del tiempo

En tu libro de texto, lee sobre la escala geológica del tiempo.

Completa la tabla.

Era	Período de tiempo	Evento biológico
1.	Hace 4.6 billones–600 millones de años	**2.**
3.	Hace 600 millones–248 millones de años	**4.**
5.	Hace 248 millones–65 millones de años	**6.**
7.	Hace 65 millones de años–presente	**8.**

En tu libro de texto, lee sobre las teorías del origen de la vida.

Completa cada enunciado.

9. La teoría de la generación espontánea asume que la vida surge espontáneamente de _____ .

10. Francesco Redi y Louis Pasteur diseñaron _____ para refutar la teoría de la generación espontánea.

11. La teoría de _____ establece que la vida proviene de vida preexistente.

12. Es probable que agregados de moléculas orgánicas hayan formado _____ , los cuales posteriormente evolucionaron y formaron las primeras células verdaderas.

Ordena los siguientes organismos del 1 al 4, según su orden evolutivo.

_____ **13.** procariotas quimiosintéticos   _____ **15.** procariotas heterótrofos

_____ **14.** eucariotas   _____ **16.** procariotas fotosintéticos productores de oxígeno

En tu libro de texto, lee sobre las pruebas y los mecanismos de la evolución.

Contesta las siguientes preguntas.

17. ¿De qué suposición se parte cuando se hace una datación relativa de fósiles? _____

_____

18. ¿Qué son estructuras homólogas? _____

_____

Cambios a través del tiempo,
continuación

Indica si cada uno de los enunciados es <u>verdadero</u> o <u>falso</u>.

_____ **19.** La evolución ocurre cuando no se altera el equilibrio genético de una población.

_____ **20.** Las mutaciones, la deriva génica y la migración pueden alterar el equilibrio genético de las poblaciones.

_____ **21.** La selección estabilizadora favorece la supervivencia de los individuos promedio para cierto rasgo.

_____ **22.** La selección disruptiva ocurre cuando se selecciona naturalmente un rasgo extremo.

_____ **23.** La radiación adaptativa ocurre cuando especies que anteriormente eran similares a una especie ancestral, se diferencian cada vez más debido a la selección natural.

En tu libro de texto, lee sobre la evolución de los primates.

Anota la letra de la columna B que corresponda al enunciado de la columna A.

Columna A	Column B
_____ **24.** Adaptación de los primates	**a.** antropoides
_____ **25.** Categoría de primates que incluye a humanos y simios	**b.** australopitecos
_____ **26.** Característica de los monos del Nuevo Mundo	**c.** género *Homo*
_____ **27.** Aparece en registros fósiles de hace dos millones de años, junto con algunas herramientas	**d.** pulgar oponible
_____ **28.** Probables antepasados humanos de 5 a 8 millones de años de antigüedad	**e.** cola prensil

En tu libro de texto, lee sobre la organización de la diversidad de la vida.

Contesta las siguientes preguntas. Consulta la clasifica- cación taxonómica del gato montés que se muestra.

29. ¿Cuál es el taxón más general en este sistema de clasificación?

_____

30. ¿Cuál es el nombre científico del gato montés?

_____

Taxón	Nombre
Reino	*Animalia*
Filo	*Chordata*
Clase	*Mammalia*
Orden	*Carnivora*
Familia	*Felidae*
Género	*Lynx*
Especie	*rufus*

Assessment
Student Recording Sheet

Standardized Test Practice

Part 1   Multiple Choice

Select the best answer from the choices given and fill in the corresponding oval.

1. Ⓐ Ⓑ Ⓒ Ⓓ   8. Ⓐ Ⓑ Ⓒ Ⓓ
2. Ⓐ Ⓑ Ⓒ Ⓓ   9. Ⓐ Ⓑ Ⓒ Ⓓ
3. Ⓐ Ⓑ Ⓒ Ⓓ   10. Ⓐ Ⓑ Ⓒ Ⓓ
4. Ⓐ Ⓑ Ⓒ Ⓓ   11. Ⓐ Ⓑ Ⓒ Ⓓ
5. Ⓐ Ⓑ Ⓒ Ⓓ   12. Ⓐ Ⓑ Ⓒ Ⓓ
6. Ⓐ Ⓑ Ⓒ Ⓓ   13. Ⓐ Ⓑ Ⓒ Ⓓ
7. Ⓐ Ⓑ Ⓒ Ⓓ

Part 2   Constructed Response/Grid In

Record your answers for Questions 14–18 on a separate sheet of paper.

Contents

Teacher Support and Planning

Teacher Support

Sequencing an Experiment

Have each student make a Foldable, using the layered-look book shown below, to sequence Miller and Urey's experiment.

How to Use the Foldable

Have students . . .

1. construct a four-page, layered-look book. *If students need additional instructions to construct a layered-look book, the bottom of this page can be reproduced and distributed to students.*

2. label the tabs *Step 1, Step 2, Step 3*, and *Results*.

3. list the three steps of Miller and Urey's experiment and the results of the experiment under the appropriate tab.

4. Use their Foldables to review what they have learned about Miller and Urey's experiment.

Going Further

- Interpret the importance of the experiment on the *Results* flap.
- Draw the experiment in three parts using *Figure 14.12* in the text as a reference.

✂ -

Layered-Look Book

STEP 1 **Collect** two sheets of paper and layer them about 1.5 cm apart vertically. Keep the edges level.

STEP 2 **Fold** up the bottom edges of the paper to form four equal tabs.

STEP 3 **Fold** the papers and crease well to hold the tabs in place. Staple along the fold. **Label** each tab.

Comparing and Contrasting Types of Natural Selection

Have each student make a Foldable, using the tri-fold book shown below, to compare and contrast the three types of natural selection.

How to Use the Foldable

Have students . . .

1. construct a tri-fold book. *If students need additional instructions to construct a tri-fold book, the bottom of this page can be reproduced and distributed to students.*
2. label each column *Stabilizing Natural Selection*, *Directional Natural Selection*, and *Disruptive Natural Selection.*
3. compare and contrast stabilizing, directional, and disruptive natural selection in each column.
4. trade their Foldables with a friend and quiz each other on the contents.

Going Further

- Draw the graphs from *Figure 15.14* in your textbook and interpret them.
- Illustrate the graphs with appropriate examples.

✂ -

Tri-Fold Book

STEP 1 **Fold** the top of a vertical piece of paper down and the bottom up to divide the paper into thirds.

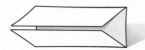

STEP 2 **Turn** the paper horizontally; **unfold** and **label** the three columns as shown.

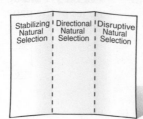

Stabilizing Natural Selection | Directional Natural Selection | Disruptive Natural Selection

Classifying Primates

Have each student make a Foldable, using the four-tab book shown below, to describe the characteristics of early *Homo* species.

How to Use the Foldable

Have students . . .

1. construct a four-tab book. *If students need additional instructions to construct a four-tab book, the bottom of this page can be reproduced and distributed to students.*

2. label the flaps *Homo habilis, Homo erectus, Neandertal,* and *Cro-Magnon.*

3. describe the characteristics of each of the early *Homo* species.

4. use their Foldables to review primates before the test.

Going Further

- Compare and contrast each of the early *Homo* species.

- Sketch an example of each *Homo* species skull beneath the appropriate flap.

✂ -

Four-Tab Book

STEP 1 **Fold** a sheet of paper in half lengthwise. Make the back edge about 1.5 cm longer than the front edge.

STEP 2 **Fold** in half, then fold in half again to make three folds.

STEP 3 **Unfold** and **cut** only the top layer along the three folds to make four tabs.

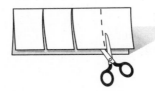

STEP 4 **Label** the tabs.

17 Organizing Life's Diversity

FOLDABLES™
Study Organizer
Use with Section 17.2

Classifying Life

Have each student make a Foldable, using the pocket book shown below, to describe the characteristics of the six kingdoms.

How to Use the Foldable

Have students . . .

1. construct a six-pocket book. *If students need additional instructions to construct a pocket book, the bottom of this page can be reproduced and distributed to students.*

2. label each pocket with one of the six kingdoms.

3. write characteristics and sketch an example of each kingdom on 3×5 index cards and place them in the pockets.

4. use their Foldables to review what they have learned about the six kingdoms.

Going Further

• Interpret the order of evolution of these organisms and explain the reasoning for that interpretation.

• Include information and sketches of additional examples of each kingdom on the index cards.

✂ --

Pocket Book

STEP 1 **Fold** a vertical 5-cm tab along the long edge of three sheets of paper.

STEP 2 **Fold** in half so the tab is on the inside.

STEP 3 **Open** the paper and glue the edges of the 5-cm tab to make a pocket. **Refold** to make a pocket book.

STEP 4 **Glue** the three pocket books together to create a six-pocket book.

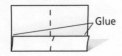
Glue

Chapter 14

MiniLab 14.1
Page 3 • Marine Fossils
Expected Results: Students should see broken cell walls of many different shapes.

Analysis
1. Answers will vary—rod-shaped, glasslike, circular, boatlike, needle-shaped, ridged or scored surface
2. Although broken, the fossil diatoms look similar and therefore have probably changed little over time.
3. The cell walls were visible because they did not decompose. The weight of water and sediments crushed them.

MiniLab 14.2
Page 4 • A Time Line

Analysis
1. the longest era—Paleozoic; the shortest era—Cenozoic
2. Mesozoic Era
3. primates

Investigate BioLab
Page 5 • Determining a Rock's Age

Data and Observations

Number of Shakes	Average
0	100
1	50
2	25
3	12
4	6
5	3

Data may vary.

Analyze and Conclude
1. K-40—penny with "head" side up; Ar-40—penny with "tail" side up
2. Potassium has 19 protons and 21 neutrons, and Argon has 18 protons and 22 neutrons; No. K-40 decays or changes into Ar-40. Remove "tail" pennies.
3. A half-life is the time needed for half the number of atoms of a radioactive element to change into atoms of a different element. Shaking the box represented a half-life.
4. They compare the amount of a radioactive element present now in a fossil or rock to the amount originally present, and use the element's half-life to calculate the sample's age.
5. a. 650 000 000
   b. 1 950 000 000
   c. 4 550 000 000
6. A small box that constricts the flipping of the coins could alter the results. If the coins are not shaken vigorously enough to get them to flip, the results could also be altered.

Reinforcement and Study Guide
Page 7 • Section 14.1
1. true
2. false
3. true
4. true
5. false
6. c
7. e
8. a
9. f
10. b
11. g
12. d
13. If rock layers, and the fossils they contain, have been left undisturbed, layers closer to the surface should be younger than those that are lower because they formed after and on top of the lower ones.
14. Relative dating will reveal only whether one fossil is older than another one.
15. radiometric dating
16. Age is determined by comparing the amount of the original radioactive element to the amount of the new element formed from decay.
17. Pre-Cambrian
18. Cenozoic
19. Mesozoic
20. Paleozoic
21. Mesozoic
22. Mesozoic
23. Mesozoic
24. Paleozoic

Reinforcement and Study Guide

Page 9 • Section 14.2

1. nonliving matter
2. spontaneous generation
3. Francesco Redi
4. disproved
5. microscope
6. microorganisms
7. spontaneously
8. Louis Pasteur
9. S-shaped
10. air
11. vital force
12. broth
13. organisms
14. biogenesis
15. does not explain
16. organic
17. oxygen
18. true
19. in the oceans
20. Oparin
21. early
22. amino acids
23. the origin of life
24. true
25. The first forms of life were probably anaerobic prokaryotes that were heterotrophs.
26. An autotroph is an organism that can make its own food. Competition for nutrients by heterotrophic prokaryotes probably led to natural selection for autotrophy.
27. Archaebacteria; many live in harsh environments and are chemosynthetic.
28. Because photosynthesis released oxygen, the concentration of that gas increased in the atmosphere.

Refuerzo y Guía de estudio

Página 11 • Sección 14.1

1. verdadero
2. falso
3. verdadero
4. verdadero
5. falso
6. c
7. e

8. a
9. f
10. b
11. g
12. d
13. Si los diferentes estratos rocosos, los fósiles que contienen, no han sido perturbados, entonces los estratos más superficiales deben ser más recientes que los estratos más profundos porque se formaron después y por encima de los más antiguos.
14. Esta técnica sólo indica si un fósil es más o menos antiguo que otro.
15. datación radiométrica
16. La edad se determina comparando la cantidad del elemento radiactivo original con respecto a la cantidad del nuevo elemento formado por desintegración.
17. Precámbrico
18. Cenozoico
19. Mesozoico
20. Paleozoico
21. Mesozoico
22. Mesozoico
23. Mesozoico
24. Paleozoico

Página 13 • Sección 14.2

1. materia inanimada
2. generación espontánea
3. Francisco Redi
4. refutó
5. microscopio
6. microorganismos
7. espontáneamente
8. Louis Pasteur
9. forma de "s"
10. aire
11. fuerza vital
12. caldo con nutrientes
13. organismos
14. biogénesis
15. no explica
16. orgánicas
17. oxígeno
18. verdadero
19. los océanos
20. Oparín

21. primitivas
22. aminoácidos
23. el origen de la vida
24. verdadero
25. Es probable que las primeras formas de vida fueran procariotas anaeróbicos heterótrofos.
26. Los autótrofos son organismos que pueden fabricar su propio alimento. La competencia por nutrientes entre los heterótrofos procariotas probablemente impulsó la aparición por selección natural de organismos autótrofos.
27. Las arquebacterias; estas bacterias viven en ambientes rigurosos y son quimiosintéticas.
28. Debido a la liberación de oxígeno elaborado a través de la fotosíntesis, la concentración de este gas aumentó en la atmósfera.

Concept Mapping
Page 15 • Formation of a Fossil

Answers may vary. Possible events chain shown.

1. Sediment piles on top of remains.
2. Sediment is compacted and cemented to form sedimentary rock.
3. Fossil brought to surface by earth movements and erosion
4. Fossil discovered
5. Fossil dated
6. Relative dating
7. Sediment layers closer to surface younger than deeper ones
8. Radiometric dating
9. Age of fossil determined by comparing amount of original radioactive element to amount of new element formed by decay

Critical Thinking
Page 16 • Section 14.1

1. E is the oldest layer in Formation 1. C' is the oldest layer in Formation 2. The two layers would be of the same age if they have similar compositions and fossil records.
2. Since layer E lies beneath layer D, fossils from layer E must be older than those in layers D and C'.
3. Because layers C and B' are probably the same age and layers D and C' are the same age, B and A' are likely the same age. Layer A is probably the newest because it is deposited on layer B, which is the same age as A' and younger than C and B',

which are younger than D and C', which are younger than E.
4. Deposition of sediment may have begun later in Formation 2. The top layer of Formation 2 may have been eroded by wind or water or may have fallen away in a landslide.

Section Focus Transparency 35
Page 17 • Inferring from Fossils

Purpose
• To illustrate how scientists gather information from fossils

Teaching Suggestions
• Project the transparency, and draw attention to the two sets of footprints.
• Discuss with students any differences in conclusions they may have drawn from their observations. Emphasize that without additional information, it is impossible to determine which conclusions were correct. Explain that scientists studying the same data sometimes interpret the data differently. Each will then look for additional information to support the conclusion.
• *Answers to questions on the transparency include:*

1. The footprints appear to be following the same path. One set of footprints disappears after the jumbled set of footprints; the other set continues.
2. Answers will vary, but students most likely will suggest that the animal belonging to the set of larger footprints was chasing the smaller animal. The jumble represents a struggle between the two animals. The smaller animal was captured by the larger animal.

Section Focus Transparency 36
Page 18 • Redi's Experiment

Purpose
• To introduce an experiment that supports biogenesis

Teaching Suggestions
• Before projecting the transparency, explain that early scientists thought that life was produced from nonliving matter. For example, by observing maggots on rotten meat, many people concluded that the meat gave rise to the maggots.
• Project the transparency, and explain that the diagram summarizes an experiment done by Francesco Redi in 1668. Point out that cloth covers the jars in

Teacher Guide & Answers

the experimental group but not in the control group. Explain that the material in the bottom of each jar is rotten meat. Also explain that maggots are immature flies.

- *Answers to questions on the transparency include:*

1. Maggots and flies are present in the control jars but not in the experimental jars.
2. Maggots are not produced by rotten meat. Flies must be present and have contact with the meat for maggots to form.

Basic Concepts Transparency 20
Page 19 • *Pasteur's Experiment*

Purpose
- To analyze Pasteur's classic experiment

Teaching Suggestions
- Before showing the transparency, discuss the theory of spontaneous generation and the general features of Pasteur's experiment. Then project the transparency and have students complete their worksheets. Discuss student responses in order to pinpoint any problems in critical thinking skills.
- Compare Pasteur's experiment with that of Redi. Have students discuss whether Pasteur's experiment supports Redi's conclusions.

Extension: Research
- Have students research the experiments and concepts of John Needham and Lazzaro Spallanzani, comparing and contrasting these with the work and concepts of Redi and Pasteur.

Answers to Student Worksheet
1. Unlike Flask A, Flask B is tilted, exposing the broth to dust particles that are trapped in the S-shaped neck. The broth in Flask B, unlike that in Flask A, subsequently becomes contaminated.
2. The independent variable is the exposure of the broth to dust particles that Pasteur suspected were the source of microorganisms.
3. The dependent variable is the growth of microorganisms in the broth.
4. Both flasks are heated to the boiling point to destroy any microorganisms that might already have contaminated the broth and to force out air that might also be contaminated. The air reenters both flasks, but dust and microorganisms are trapped in the curve of the neck.
5. Yes; the experiment showed that air contained no vital force that could give rise to life, since the broth

in Flask A was exposed to air but did not become contaminated. The microorganisms that developed in Flask B arose from other microorganisms.
6. Answers will vary but students may suggest an open straight-necked flask containing broth, which is boiled. Like the tilted flask, the straight-necked flask will show the growth of microorganisms.
7. It supports biogenesis, the hypothesis that living organisms develop only from other living organisms.

Reteaching Skills Transparency 23
Page 21 • *Geologic Time Scale*

Purpose
- To illustrate a time scale for the history of life on Earth
- Skill: Sequencing

Teaching Suggestions
- The length of geologic time is a difficult concept for many students. Explain that if all geologic time were equal to one month, humans have been in existence for only about the last two minutes of the month.
- To reinforce understanding and learning of the transparency, line students up and give each either a date or an event from the geologic time scale. Allow students to sort out and sequence the times and events of the scale for themselves. Then discuss and, if necessary, correct their work.
- Discuss methods of dating of fossils and sediments that have contributed to the construction of the geologic time scale. Emphasize that the scale is neither arbitrary nor uniform, since it is based on the fossil record.

Extension: Model
- Have students work in cooperative groups to construct a scale model of the geologic time scale. The model should include boundaries between eras and periods as well as information concerning the evolution or extinction of various organisms during each time segment. The model will have to be relatively large to accommodate recent events such as the evolution of primates.

Answers to Student Worksheet
1. The geologic time scale is based on fossil evidence in Earth's rocks and the age of the rocks.
2. The geologic time scale is divided into four large sections. Three of these sections are eras, which have subdivisions called periods.

3. Fossil evidence suggests that forms of life, possibly photosynthetic bacteria, had evolved between 3.9 and 3.4 billion years ago in the Precambrian.

4. The Cambrian Period was dominated by marine invertebrates such as marine worms, primitive arthropods, and echinoderms.

5. The first vertebrates, primitive fish, evolved in the Paleozoic Era.

6. Since the K-T boundary is located at a time about 65 million years ago, this is when most if not all dinosaurs became extinct.

7. Based on fossil evidence thus far discovered, birds did not evolve until about 150 million years ago.

8. The Permian layers would be above the 320-million-year-old Carboniferous, and the Devonian layers would be below.

Chapter Assessment
Page 23 • Reviewing Vocabulary

1. spontaneous generation
2. biogenesis
3. Fossils
4. protocells
5. archaebacteria
6. plate tectonics

Page 24 • Understanding Main Ideas (Part A)

1. b   5. d
2. a   6. c
3. a   7. c
4. b

Page 25 • Understanding Main Ideas (Part B)

1. c   2. b

3. According to the theory of continental drift, the continents have moved during Earth's history and are still moving. The continents move because they ride on Earth's crust, which consists of several rigid plates that drift on top of molten rock.

4. The photoautotrophs released oxygen, which was missing from the ancient atmosphere and necessary for aerobic respiration. Thus, the autotrophs produced the O_2 needed for the aerobic organisms to evolve.

Page 26 • Thinking Critically

1. 50 grams   5. 50 grams
2. 25 grams   6. 75 grams
3. 12.5 grams   7. 87.5 grams
4. 6.25 grams   8. 93.75 grams

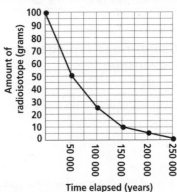

Years Passed vs. Amount of Radioisotope

Page 27 • Applying Scientific Methods

1. In order to determine the age of fossil A, scientists could use an absolute dating technique called radiometric dating. It relies on the rate at which unstable radioactive nuclei break down and, over time, give off radiation and eventually become different, stable elements. The ratio of the amount of unstable radioisotope to the amount of the stable end product allows scientists to calculate how much time has passed since the fish was alive. Another method, relative dating, relies on scientists knowing the age of fossils above, below, or within the same layer as the unknown specimen. The age of fossil A can then be estimated.

2. The leaf fossils in layer IV would indicate that this area was dry land with plants growing. The fish fossils in layers III and II indicate that the area was later under water and supported aquatic life. Layer I has no visible fossils. This could indicate that the area was a desert with little life and no water present to allow large numbers of fossils to form, or the area could have been covered by ice so that there were no life forms to be preserved.

3. Photoautotrophs evolved and released O_2 into the atmosphere.

4. Photoautotrophs released O_2 into the atmosphere. Prior to that, there was no large source of atmospheric oxygen.

5. At this stage in Earth's history, aerobic organisms evolved.

6. The evolution of aerobes caused a decline in the amount of atmospheric oxygen.

7. They could look for fossils of cyanobacteria (photoautotrophs) and aerobic organisms.

Student Recording Sheet
Page 29

Answers can be found on page 390 in the Teacher Wraparound Edition.

Chapter 15

MiniLab 15.1
Page 33 • Camouflage Provides an Adaptive Advantage

Expected Results

Most groups will have picked up more white dots than black dots.

Analysis

1. white dots
2. Light-colored insects may be seen and preyed on more easily than dark-colored insects. Therefore, dark-colored insects have a higher survival rate.
3. Over time, an insect population might become dark-colored because light-colored insects were eliminated from the population.

MiniLab 15.2
Page 34 • Detecting a Variation

Data and Observations

Student data should indicate a wide range in shell length. There should be few shells at either extreme and the majority of shells should fall in the middle range of the measurements.

Analysis

1. yes—student answers will vary
2. Directional selection—larger shells may favor the survival of offspring because they may contain larger, more viable seeds.

Internet BioLab
Page 35 • Natural Selection and Allelic Frequency

Data and Observations

Make sure students are correctly calculating allelic frequency after each "generation" and recording these data in their data tables. Students should observe changes in the allelic frequencies of the rabbit population. Student graphs should show an increase in the frequency of the G allele and a decrease in the g allele.

Analyze and Conclude

1. Neither allele disappeared from the population because the g allele is also in the heterozygous (Gg) rabbits.
2. The graph shows an increase in the frequency of the G allele and a decrease in the frequency of the g allele due to natural selection against white rabbits.

3. There would be less selective pressure on white rabbits and, therefore, less decline in the frequency of the g allele.
4. Students should notice little difference in the allelic frequencies posted on the Internet and the frequencies they calculated. By combining data, students may get more accurate results.

Reinforcement and Study Guide
Page 37 • Section 15.1

1. true
2. false
3. false
4. true
5. false
6. false
7. Overproduction of Offspring
8. Struggle for Existence
9. Variation
10. Natural Selection
11. camouflage
12. mimicry
13. camouflage
14. both
15. mimicry
16. homologous structure
17. embryological development
18. homologous structure
19. vestigial structure
20. genetic comparisons
21. analogous structure
22. vestigial structure

Reinforcement and Study Guide
Page 39 • Section 15.2

1. true
2. Darwin
3. phenotype
4. populations
5. gene pool
6. genotypes
7. does not change
8. true
9. genes
10. mutations
11. true
12. drift
13. small
14. natural selection

15. directional selection
16. Speciation
17. Reproductive isolation
18. reproductive isolation
19. gradualism
20. fossil
21. punctuated equilibrium
22. Speciation occurred, with each species adapting to a different food source.
23. the process of evolution of an ancestral species into an array of species that occupy different niches
24. It occurs when species begin to adapt to different environments and change according to the pressures of natural selection.
25. when unrelated organisms occupy similar environments and face similar selection pressures

Refuerzo y Guía de estudio
Página 41 • Sección 15.1

1. verdadero
2. falso
3. falso
4. verdadero
5. falso
6. falso
7. sobreproducción de crías
8. lucha por la existencia
9. variabilidad
10. selección natural
11. camuflaje
12. mimetismo
13. camuflaje
14. ambas
15. mimetismo
16. estructura homóloga
17. desarrollo embrionario
18. estructura homóloga
19. estructura vestigial
20. comparación genética
21. estructura análoga
22. estructura vestigial

Página 43 • Sección 15.2

1. verdadero
2. Darwin
3. fenotipo
4. las poblaciones

5. el caudal genético
6. genotipos
7. no cambian
8. verdadero
9. los genes
10. mutaciones
11. verdadero
12. la deriva genética
13. pequeñas
14. selección natural
15. selección direccional
16. especiación
17. aislamiento reproductor
18. aislamiento reproductor
19. gradualismo
20. fósil
21. equilibrio interrumpido
22. Ocurrió especiación. Cada especie se adaptó a un tipo diferente de alimento.
23. Es el proceso de evolución de una especie ancestral en un conjunto de especies que ocupan diferentes nichos.
24. Ocurre cuando una especie se adapta a diferentes ambientes y cambia debido a los efectos de la selección natural.
25. Ocurre cuando organismos no relacionados ocupan ambientes similares y encuentran presiones selectivas similares.

Concept Mapping
Page 45 • Evidence of Evolution

1. Fossils
2. anatomy
3. embryology
4. fossil bones
5. homologous structures
6. nucleotide sequences

Critical Thinking
Page 46 • Sections 15.1, 15.2

1. There would be fewer TB cells because of the absence of selection pressure of the drug. Mutated cells without the enzyme would have no survival advantage.
2. The HIV virus mutates into an AZT-resistant strain, the spread of which is encouraged by the presence of AZT.
3. The mutated AZT-resistant strain may not be resistant to ddI.

4. The virus will mutate three times in response to the selection pressure of each drug. Although resistant to the three drugs, the mutated virus may not be able to replicate.

Section Focus Transparency 37
Page 47 • Camouflage

Purpose
- To illustrate how adaptation aids the chances of survival

Teaching Suggestions
- Project the transparency, and draw attention to the difference in color of the two snowshoe hares. Point out that the two hares are the same species. Explain that the color of this species changes from summer to winter.
- *Answers to questions on the transparency include:*
  1. The color change enables the hare to blend in with its environment, thus providing better protection from predators.
  2. Answers will vary, but might include: The skin of the flounder makes it blend in with the ocean floor where it lives, and a walkingstick insect is shaped like the shrub branches it rests on.

Section Focus Transparency 38
Page 48 • Evolving Populations

Purpose
- To introduce the relationship between natural selection and variation in populations

Teaching Suggestions
- Project the transparency, and ask students what adaptations fish living in these streams might have to aid survival. Lead students to recognize that some fish most likely would be camouflaged to blend in with the bottom of the stream.
- Discuss with students the disadvantage that fish moved from Stream A to Stream B might encounter. Point out that since the rocks on the bottom of Stream A are lighter than those of Stream B, fish that are camouflaged for protection in Stream A would be more easily seen in Stream B.
- *Answers to questions on the transparency include:*
  1. The rocks on the bottom of Stream A are lighter in color than those in Stream B.

2. The fish in Stream B might become darker over time.

Basic Concepts Transparency 21
Page 49 • Genetic Equilibrium

Purpose
- To review the inheritance pattern of incomplete dominance and illustrate the concept of genetic equilibrium

Teaching Suggestions
- Project the transparency and have the students compare and contrast the data as they relate to genetic equilibrium.
- Point out that the transparency illustrates an inheritance pattern, incomplete dominance, and a concept, genetic equilibrium.
- Make sure the students realize that the concept of genetic equilibrium holds true regardless of the way traits are inherited.

Extension: Critical Thinking
- Have students question whether genetic equilibrium can exist in nature. Students should recognize that, because mutations occur regularly and frequently in a population, genetic equilibrium rarely, if ever, occurs in nature. In fact, all populations evolve.

Answers to Student Worksheet
1. The pattern of heredity is incomplete dominance, which produces three phenotypes.
2. To determine if a population is in genetic equilibrium, one must calculate allelic frequencies. Allelic frequencies can be determined only if the heterozygous individuals and homozygous dominant individuals can be differentiated, as is the case in the pattern of heredity known as incomplete dominance.
3. The phenotypic frequency—the percent of each phenotype in the population—differs in the two generations.
4. The population is said to be in genetic equilibrium because the allelic frequencies, the percentages of the R and R' alleles, do not vary between the generations.
5. The population would be viewed as not evolving because no traits are developing or being eliminated from the population.
6. Genetic drift would alter allelic frequencies through crossing over during meiosis or through other chance events.

7. A mutation will change the allelic frequency in the population to some degree and thus alter the genetic equilibrium of the population.

Basic Concepts Transparency 22
Page 51 • *Variation in Populations*

Purpose
- To show the types of natural selection that act upon variations in organisms

Teaching Suggestions
- Project the transparency and have students compare, contrast, and interpret the curves shown.

- Remind students that natural selection involves the adapting of organisms in a population to their existing environment or to changes in the environment.

- Lead students in a discussion of the advantages and disadvantages of the three types of natural selection illustrated in the transparency.

Extension: Research
- Have students research the evolutionary history of a phylum, family, or class of organisms and describe how specific adaptations appear to have been favored by a particular type(s) of natural selection.

Answers to Student Worksheet

1. Stabilizing selection favors average individuals. As is shown by the sizes of spiders in the graph, stabilizing selection reduces variation in a population.

2. Directional selection favors one or the other extreme form of a trait, as shown by the selection for longer beaks among the woodpeckers. This type of selection can result in rapid evolutionary change within the population.

3. Disruptive selection favors both extremes of a trait, such as light and dark color in limpets. If there are no intermediate forms, disruptive selection can lead to the evolution of two distinct species.

4. Large spiders might be more conspicuous and therefore more vulnerable to predation, and small spiders might be at a disadvantage in terms of capturing sufficient prey.

5. If the longer beak enabled woodpeckers to find more insects by probing deeper into the bark of trees, these woodpeckers would have a greater chance of surviving and reproducing than other members of the population.

6. Predators would be able to spot a tan limpet against either a light-colored rock or a dark-colored rock, backgrounds that would favor white limpets and brown limpets respectively.

7. By acting on variations, they all cause changes in gene pools, and alter allelic frequencies from one generation to the next.

Reteaching Skills Transparency 24
Page 53 • *Role of Isolation in Speciation*

Purpose
- To study speciation in action
- Skill: Recognizing cause and effect

Teaching Suggestions
- Present the transparency and explain the research taking place on the island of Hawaii. There, the activities of Mauna Loa and Kilauea volcanoes produce isolated regions Hawaiians call *kipukas*, or "islands of survival" surrounded by lava flows. Professor Ken Kaneshiro studies how isolation affects "picture-wing" *Drosophila* in kipukas formed on Mauna Loa about 140 years ago. Because the *Drosophila* populations are small, there should be more inbreeding, introducing new variations in genes in the population. After a long time, new species should arise.

  But Kaneshiro is finding significant changes in *Drosophila* genes much sooner than expected. He has a tentative hypothesis. *Drosophila* courtship lasts about 15 minutes. (The student worksheet drawing shows one of the "steps"—the male buzzes his wing in a courting song.) If a male does not perform courtship well, a female will reject him. In a kipuka, however, females seem to become less demanding. Males that had little chance to mate now contribute their genes, introducing new variations. This speeds up the rate of evolutionary change.

- Note: Researchers have learned which regions of the *Drosophila* brain control steps of the mating ritual. Variations in the genes that form that area may result in variations in courtship behavior.

Extension: Research Report
- Have students research other examples of "evolution in action." Examples include the flightless birds of the Pacific islands, vertical speciation in rain forests, and lizard species in the Caribbean islands.

Answers to Student Worksheet

1. Speciation is the evolution of new species. In the kipukas, the changes in genetic frequencies indicate that one day new Drosophila species may arise.

2. Geographic isolation occurs if a physical barrier separates a population into groups. The kipukas were isolated by lava flows from Mauna Loa.

3. Reproductive isolation occurs when formerly interbreeding organisms are prevented from producing fertile offspring. In the future, the Drosophila from the kipukas and those from the forest may become unable or unwilling to mate.

4. Because of mutations, the order of the genes has changed. Changes like this lead to new species when the genetic material becomes different enough to create reproductive isolation.

5. Birds can fly in and out of a kipuka; changes may not be due to geographic isolation.

Chapter Assessment
Page 55 • Reviewing Vocabulary

1. Artificial selection
2. camouflage
3. mimicry
4. gene pool
5. allelic frequency
6. genetic drift
7. Stabilizing selection
8. polyploid
9. Natural selection
10. punctuated equilibrium
11. vestigial structure
12. adaptive radiation

Page 56 • Understanding Main Ideas (Part A)

1. d   4. d
2. c   5. a
3. a   6. a

Page 57 • Understanding Main Ideas (Part B)

1. c   4. b
2. d   5. c
3. c   6. b

Page 58 • Thinking Critically

1. The light-colored squirrels blend in well with the soil found in the area and with the leaves that fall from the trees and cover the ground in the autumn. The darker-colored squirrels blend in well with the paved walkways of the park area and also with the darkened tree trunks. The medium-colored squirrels would be more visible to predators and thus be selected against.

2. After a long period of time, squirrels with the once most common phenotype, medium fur color, will produce fewer and fewer offspring and will gradually be eradicated. The light- and dark-colored individuals will live and reproduce successfully. After a while, disruptive selection will concentrate the color distribution at the two extremes. Eventually, the two groups may no longer recognize each other for mating purposes. This reproductive isolation could lead to the two types becoming separate species. Another possibility with the same end result is that these squirrels would tend to survive most successfully in areas where either dark or light coat color variation would be most advantageous. This would lead to geographic isolation.

Page 59 • Appying Scientific Methods

1. It would be reasonable to expect that the flies would move either directly upward toward food or directly downward toward food because there wasn't anything for them to eat in-between those areas.

2. You should end up with two different types of flies. One type will consistently fly only upward and the other will fly only downward.

3. Disruptive selection would be operating. The two extremes are being favored, while the middle choice and "no preference" files are being selected against. This is true because the middle and "no preference" flies are being discarded in the experiment, while the two extremes are being retained and allowed to mate.

4. The frequency of the allele for negative geotaxis would be increasing.

5. The preferred foods could ripen at different times, so that at one point in the year it would be beneficial to fly upward and at a different time of the year it would be more productive to fly downward. It might be, for example, that they feed on the pollen or other product of a particular species of flower. The flower may open only in the evening. So at that time of the day, the fly would do better

to fly upward toward the flower. At other times, the fly may do better moving downward. There could also be a variety of predators that feed on the flies. Perhaps some of these predators also have preferred niches that are related to height levels in the vegetation.

6. Eventually the two populations would become reproductively isolated owing to their height preferences. Two distinct species with their separate gene pools would result.

Student Recording Sheet

Page 61

Answers can be found on page 418 in the Teacher Wraparound Edition.

Chapter 16

MiniLab 16.1
Page 65 • How useful is an opposable thumb?

Analysis

1. Performance should be better with the use of an opposable thumb.

2. Primates with opposable thumbs can use tools and climb.

3. Student models will vary, but should complete the task without the use of an opposable thumb.

MiniLab 16.2
Page 66 • Compare Human Proteins with Those of Other Primates

Expected Results

The human, chimpanzee, and gorilla sequences are identical. Baboons differ by 33 percent and lemurs by 47 percent.

Analysis

1. gorilla and chimpanzee; lemur

2. Baboons should branch off lemurs. Gorillas, chimpanzees, and humans should be close together.

Investigate BioLab
Page 67 • Comparing Skulls of Three Primates

Data Table

	Gorilla	Australopithecus	Modern human
1.	32 cm^2	19 cm^2	12 cm^2
2.	23 cm^2	23 cm^2	40 cm^2
3.	Smaller	Larger	Larger
4.	No	No	Yes
5.	600 cm^3	600 cm^3	1060 cm^3
6.	35	55	90
7.	Yes	Yes	No
8.	Yes	Yes	No
9.	Yes	Yes	No

Analyze and Conclude

1. Humans have a small facial area compared with brain area. Apes have a large facial area compared with brain area. Australopithecines were intermediate between apes and humans but closer to apes.

2. Apes have a small cranial capacity, whereas humans have a large cranial capacity, and that of australopithecines was intermediate but closer to the apes. An ape has a small jaw angle, and a human has a large jaw angle. The jaw angle of australopithecines was intermediate but closer to that of the ape.

3. Each of the items in the data table indicates anatomical similarities that have undergone change.

4. Possible sources include measuring incorrectly, rounding errors, and errors from measuring a single example rather than taking a mean of many fossil measurements.

Real World BioApplications
Page 71 • Analyzing Lower Back Disorders

Planning the Activity

Use this activity with Chapter 16, after students have been introduced to the concept of bipedal.

Purpose

Students compare the skeletal and muscular structure of apes and humans to determine if walking upright is the root of back pain.

Career Applications

This activity reflects the knowledge, critical thinking, and problem-solving skills desirable in health care careers such as physical therapist, recreational therapist, and personal trainer. These critical thinking and problem-solving skills are also desirable for physical therapist assistants and aides who perform specific procedures and related tasks under the supervision of a physical therapist. Treatment procedures delegated to physical therapist assistants may involve exercises, massage, electrical stimulation, paraffin baths, hot/cold packs, traction, and ultrasound. Assistants record the patient's progress during treatment and report the outcome of each treatment to the physical therapist.

All of the services are designed for patients to help improve mobility, relieve pain, and prevent or limit permanent physical disabilities. The patients typically include accident victims and individuals with disabling conditions such as lower back pain, arthritis, heart disease, fractures, head injuries, and cerebral palsy.

Teaching Suggestions

- After students have read the introduction, review the information about walking upright presented in the text.

- As students start the activity, discuss the similarities and differences of the gorilla skeleton and the human skeleton.

- You may wish to invite volunteers to demonstrate each of the exercises in Part B. As each exercise is demonstrated, ask a second volunteer to identify the vertebral area most influenced by the exercise.

Answers to Student Worksheet

Part A

1. Check to make sure the lumbar area of the spine is circled in the drawing on the right.

2. The spine of the gorilla appears to be relatively straight in the walking position. The spine of the human appears to curve toward the front of the body in the cervical (neck) area and toward the back of the body in the thoracic (chest) area in the walking position.

3. Student answers may vary. Most students will state that the stress probably causes muscles to cramp or become nonsupportive, and nerves to become irritated.

4. Student answers may vary. Most students will reason that the great weight and stress will cause the most damage or discomfort to that area of the back.

Part B

Students should choose exercises 2, 3, 4, 5, 9, and 10.

Analyze and Conclude

1. Back pain can cause nerves that lead to many parts of the body to become inflamed, so a slight movement can cause great pain. Also, since most of the body's weight is supported by the lumbar region of the spine, people may find it difficult to do anything in a standing position.

2. Students should have chosen the exercises that affect the lower back and its supportive muscles. The other exercises listed are valid exercises but do not focus on the lower back. Student answers may vary, but most students should list strengthening and increasing flexibility of the supportive lower back muscles as the reason for choosing the exercises.

Reinforcement and Study Guide
Page 73 • Section 16.1

1. primate characteristic
2. primate characteristic
3. not a primate characteristic
4. primate characteristic
5. primate characteristic
6. not a primate characteristic
7. primate characteristic
8. primate characteristic
9. not a primate characteristic
10. primate characteristic
11. not a primate characteristic
12. not a primate characteristic
13. primate characteristic
14. primate characteristic
15. not a primate characteristic
16. not a primate characteristic
17. primate characteristic
18. not a primate characteristic
19. primate characteristic
20. primate characteristic
21. false
22. true
23. false
24. true
25. false
26. baboon, Old World monkey
27. spider monkey, New World monkey
28. tarsier, haplorhine
29. They may all share a common ancestor.
30. New World monkeys; about 30 to 35 million years ago
31. the fossil record and comparative study of living primates
32. During the Miocene Period, when Old World monkeys evolved, the fossil record indicates that global temperatures were dropping.
33. DNA analysis suggest that gibbons were probably the first apes to evolve, followed by the orangutans, African apes, gorillas, and chimpanzees.

Reinforcement and Study Guide
Page 75 • Section 16.2

1. an early hominid that lived in Africa
2. *Australopithecus africanus*

3. It had a foramen magnum that was located at the bottom of the skull, as in humans.

4. The organism must have walked upright.

5. *A. afarensis*

6. chimpanzee

7. human

8. true

9. false

10. false

11. true

12. false

13. false

14. true

15. b

16. a

17. d

18. a

19. b

20. d

21. a

22. Neandertals

23. Cro-Magnons

24. Neandertals

25. both

26. Cro-Magnons

Refuerzo y Guía de estudio
Página 77 • Sección 16.1

1. Sí

2. Sí

3. No

4. Sí

5. Sí

6. No

7. Sí

8. Sí

9. No

10. Sí

11. No

12. No

13. Sí

14. Sí

15. No

16. No

17. Sí

18. No

19. Sí

20. Sí

21. falso

22. verdadero

23. falso

24. verdadero

25. falso

26. babuino; mono del Viejo Mundo

27. mono araña; mono del Nuevo Mundo

28. társido; haplorhine

29. Que todos ellos comparten un antepasado común.

30. Los monos del Nuevo Mundo; aparecieron hace entre 30 y 35 millones de años.

31. En el registro fósil y en el estudio comparativo de los primates actuales.

32. Durante el Mioceno, cuando aparecieron los monos del Viejo Mundo, el registro fósil indica que las temperaturas globales estaban bajando.

33. El análisis del DNA sugiere que los gibones fueron los primeros simios que aparecieron, seguidos de los orangutanes, los simios africanos, los gorilas y los chimpancés.

Página 79 • Sección 16.2

1. Un homínido primitivo que vivió en África.

2. *Australopithecus africanus*

3. Su foramen magnum estaba localizado en la base del cráneo, como en los humanos.

4. Le indicó que este organismo caminaba en posición erecta.

5. *A. afarensis*

6. chimpancé

7. humano

8. verdadero

9. falso

10. falso

11. verdadero

12. falso

13. falso

14. verdadero

15. b

16. a

17. d

18. a

19. b

20. d

21. a

22. neandertales

23. cromañones

24. neandertales

25. ambos

26. cromañones

Concept Mapping
Page 81 • Characteristics of Primates

1. large brain
2. binocular vision
3. opposable thumb
4. flexible joints
5. complex mental functions
6. face forward
7. grasping and clinging
8. ball-and-socket structure
9. hip
10. shoulder
11. memory
12. perception
13. hands
14. depth
15. distance
16. mobility
17. eating
18. use of tools

Critical Thinking
Page 82 • Section 16.2

1. Accept logical answers. Possibilities include looking for hominid tooth marks on animal bones or investigating whether the types of tools found in the caves could have been used as weapons to kill the animals found there.
2. Answers will vary. Brain may have wondered why hominids with teeth typical of plant eaters would consume meat, and why they would capture and consume carnivores, which are much more dangerous to hunt than herbivorous animals.
3. The hominids were probably included in the prey of the carnivores. Students might also suggest that both hominids and carnivorous animals fed at the same site.
4. It supports Brain's theory because it indicates that a hominid was killed by a leopard, rather than a leopard being killed by a hominid.

Section Focus Transparency 39
Page 83 • Comparing Hands

Purpose
- To compare and contrast primate hands with those of other mammals

Teaching Suggestions
- Project the transparency, and identify each hand. Have students describe the characteristics of each.
- Explain that the chimpanzee and the baboon are primates, a group of mammals that students will learn about in this section. Tell students that humans also belong to this group. Ask students what other characteristics primates share. (Answers will vary, but might include fingernails, large brain, and flexible arm and shoulder joints.)
- *Answers to questions on the transparency include:*
  1. They both have five fingers, fingernails, and a thumb that sticks out from the other fingers at an angle. The squirrel hand has four fingers and no thumb.
  2. The chimpanzee probably can grasp things more tightly and move its fingers more easily.

Section Focus Transparency 40
Page 84 • Skeletal Clues

Purpose
- To compare and contrast gorilla and australopithecine skeletons

Teaching Suggestions
- Project the transparency, and have students observe the similarities and differences between the two skeletons.
- Explain that an australopithecine is an early primate that lived in Africa and had apelike and humanlike characteristics. Ask students to suggest ways in which an australopithecine was humanlike and ways in which it was apelike. (Humanlike—spine is S-shaped; arms shorter than legs; wider, flatter pelvis. Apelike—smaller braincase)
- *Answers to questions on the transparency include:*
  1. The long arms and hand structure of the gorilla skeleton suggest that these animals walked on all four limbs at times. For australopithecines, the shorter arms, structure of the hands, and position where the spinal column attaches to the skull suggest that they walked in an upright position.
  2. Walking on two feet in an upright position leaves the arms and hands free for using tools.

Teacher Guide & Answers

Basic Concepts Transparency 23
Page 85 • *Possible Phylogeny of Humans*

Purpose
- To show one possible view of the evolutionary path to modern humans

Teaching Suggestions
- Project the transparency and discuss its content. Include in the discussion reference to bipedalism, tool use, and brain size.
- Explain that modern humans did not evolve from modern apes such as gorillas, chimpanzees, or orangutans. Paleoanthropologists suggest that sometime prior to four or five million years ago modern apes and hominids branched from a common ancestor.
- Review procedures and methods used to determine the age of ancient fossils such as those of early hominids.

Extension: Role Play
- Organize students into groups. Have each group create a brief skit of a "day in the life" of each species of hominid represented in the transparency. Have them use their text and do outside research for clues about the behavior and living conditions of the different species.

Answers to Student Worksheet
1. The earliest known hominid is Australopithecus afarensis, whose fossils date back to three or four million years ago.
2. Approximately three million years passed between the appearance of the first hominid and the first Homo sapiens.
3. The australopithecines became extinct about 2–2.5 million years ago.
4. According to the transparency, Paranthropus robustus and Paranthropus boisei did not belong to the branch that led to modern humans.
5. Homo erectus may have been the first hominids to use fire.
6. The diagram supports the view that Neandertals were not part of the direct ancestral line to modern humans but rather were a side branch.
7. Bipedalism allows for the free use of hands, which may have led to the development of tool-using.

Reteaching Skills Transparency 25
Page 87 • *Human Versus Primate Traits*

Purpose
- To review human evolution and explore the differences between humans and apes
- Skill: Comparing and contrasting

Teaching Suggestions
- Present the transparency. Tell students that these skulls are not drawn to scale, so that they appear to be the same size. To analyze the information more accurately, they need to note the information about the size of the braincase, indicated below each drawing.
- Point out the physical structures that biologists would compare when analyzing evolutionary patterns. This transparency emphasizes these structures: size of the braincase, which may be indicated by the angle of the forehead and the size of the head; the presence and prominence of brow ridges above the eyes; size and shape of the jaw; tooth size and structure.
- Discuss similarities between the various skulls and modern human and ape skulls.

Extension: Research Report
- Have students select one of the groups shown on the transparency or mentioned in the text and write a research report about that group. They will be searching for information about the "lifestyle" of the group—such things as its local geography, food source, and social makeup. Students with aptitudes in art may choose to illustrate their selections through paintings or sculptures based upon their research.

Answers to Student Worksheet
1. a. A. afarensis; with ape: <u>braincase</u>: about same size; <u>teeth</u>: seem similar; <u>facial structure</u>: angle about the same; with human: <u>braincase</u>: about 800 cm³ smaller; <u>teeth</u>: has sharp canine teeth; <u>facial structure</u>: much greater angle; prominent brows.

   b. H. habilis; with ape: <u>braincase</u>: about 100–200 cm³ larger; <u>teeth</u>: no sharp canine teeth; <u>facial structure</u>: less angle; with human: <u>braincase</u>: about 600–700 cm³ smaller; <u>teeth</u>: seem similar; <u>facial structure</u>: greater angle; brows more prominent.

   c. Neandertal; with ape: <u>braincase</u>: about 900 cm³ larger; <u>teeth</u>: no sharp canine teeth; <u>facial structure</u>: much less angle; *with human:*

braincase: 100 cm³ larger; <u>teeth</u>: seem similar; <u>facial structure</u>: angles about the same; brows much more prominent.

  d. Cro-Magnon; with ape: <u>braincase</u>: about 850 cm³ larger; <u>teeth</u>: no sharp canine teeth; <u>facial structure</u>: much less angle; with human: <u>braincase</u>: about the same; <u>teeth</u>: about the same; <u>facial structure</u>: about the same.

2. Bipedalism leaves the arms and hands free for other activities such as using tools and carrying items.

Chapter Assessment
Page 89 • Reviewing Vocabulary

1. bipedal
2. primates
3. opposable thumb
4. haplorhines
5. prehensile tail
6. hominids
7. australopithecines
8. Neandertals
9. Cro-Magnons

Page 91 • Understanding Main Ideas (Part A)

1. c
2. d
3. c
4. a
5. b
6. c
7. a
8. c
9. d
10. a

Page 92 • Understanding Main Ideas (Part B)

1. b
2. d
3. c
4. b
5. c
6. a

Page 93 • Thinking Critically

1. Successful primate adaptations for arboreal life include binocular vision, an opposable thumb, the rotating ball-and-socket shoulder joint, and in some cases, the prehensile tail. All but the last adaptation have been significant in the evolution of hominids. Binocular vision permits depth perception, which is critical for tree life, allows for better judgment of predator and prey distances, and also makes the fashioning of tools possible. The opposable thumb makes grasping and crafting tools possible. The flexible shoulder joint made movement through the trees easier for primates and, for hominids, was a necessary step in the evolution of efficient arm movements.

2. Being bipedal allowed hominids to use their hands for tasks other than locomotion, such as tool-making and food-gathering.

3. Ape jaws are larger and heavier than hominid jaws. Apes have large teeth with big canines. The basic shape of the ape jaw is not as rounded as that of a hominid.

4. The fossil record is not complete. Many of our interpretations of which primate or hominid preceded the other is based on fragments of skeletons. In addition, ancient human fossils are rare due to poor conditions for fossilization at most of the sites.

Page 94 • Applying Scientific Methods

1. The silicate deposits indicate a relatively dry grassland environment. This hypothesis is reinforced by the computer models predicting cool, dry air being diverted toward Africa as ice sheets grew in the Northern Hemisphere.

2. The African habitat had changed from grassland back to large expanses of forest. This change would have been due to the recession of the ice sheets in the Northern Hemisphere, which resulted in a climate change from cool and dry to warm and moist. The warmer air could hold more moisture. Also, core samples did not contain silicates and dust deposits 2 million years ago, indicating that large expanses of grassland were no longer present.

3. The presence of volcanic ash in the cores and in the Rift valley allows for a more precise time correlation between hominid fossils found on land and the climatic record provided by the ocean cores.

4. By eating meat, the chances of survival were greatly increased since meat is available year-round. Thus, eating a variety of foods, including meat, enhanced the quality of their diet.

5. The jaw of a vegetarian animal is necessarily heavy

with broad, flat teeth. This allows for the chewing and grinding necessary to prepare the food for further digestion. The tooth and jaw structure of an omnivore or a carnivore does not require the same massive structure. Meat does not require the same amount and kind of mechanical processing. A meat-eater would also need teeth modified for tearing the flesh of the animals consumed.

Student Recording Sheet
Page 95
Answers can be found on page 440 in the Teacher Wraparound Edition.

Chapter 17

MiniLab 17.1
Page 99 • Using a Dichotomous Key in a Field Investigation

Analysis

1. identification of organisms
2. vein and margin structure, leaf shape and size, number of lobes
3. more specific

MiniLab 17.2
Page 100 • Using a Cladogram to Show Relationships

Analysis

1. Students will complete the cladogram as follows: node 1 = hole in hip socket, node 4 = extension of pubis bone, node 5 = unequal enamel, node 6 = skull shelf.
2. Dinosaur F shares 1 trait with C, 2 traits with D, and 3 traits with E.
3. three-toed hind foot; grasping hand; extension of pubis bone
4. broader—hole in hip socket extends to all 7 animals; smaller—three-toed hind foot extends to only 1 clad

Investigate BioLab
Page 101 • Making a Dichotomous Key

Data and Observations

Have students exchange their keys. If another group can use them, their accuracy is confirmed.

Analysis

1. The keys may or may not have been alike. The groups may have first divided the beetles into groups based on different features, such as size rather than color.
2. Useful: size, color, and shape of various body parts, number of body sections, and antennae features; not useful: number of legs, number of antennae, habitat.
3. Having only two choices makes it easy to analyze organisms. In many keys, the choice is that the organism either has or does not have a particular characteristic.

Real World BioApplications
Page 103 • A Dichotomous Key

Planning the Activity

This activity can be used with Chapter 17, after students have been introduced to a variety of classification schemes.

Purpose

Students apply their critical thinking skills to develop a dichotomous key for identifying cockroaches.

Career Applications

The critical thinking skills of comparing and contrasting, highlighted in this activity, have career applications in the areas of wildlife management, pest control management, field ecology, and open lands stewardship. A wetland delineation assistant is an example of a technical occupation heavily dependent on using dichotomous keys. In many instances, state or federal guidelines require that a survey of flora and fauna in a wetlands area be completed before development plans are approved. Assistants work with plant and animal taxonomists, botanists, and environmental engineers to document the plants existing in the area designated for development. Assistants must have a keen eye and a good sense of detail to successfully catalog species in an area.

Teaching Suggestions

- After students have read the classification materials in the text, discuss with them the various methods used to classify living organisms. Lead the discussion to the conclusion that all classifications can be accomplished by formulating a question that can be answered "yes" or "no."

- Direct students to read the activity introduction. Then discuss the partial key shown in Part A. Model for students how to use the key.

- Encourage students to look up the term *dichotomous* in the dictionary. Have them explain why the term is applied to the key described in this activity.

Answers to Student Worksheet

Part A

1. 1a, Has 8 legs or fewer; 2a, Has 8 legs; 3a, Is brown: TRAP-DOOR SPIDER
2. Answers may vary. Possible answers include size, color, markings, and physical differences among structural characteristics, such as wing length or shape.

Part B

Students' dichotomous keys may vary. Each key should have a dichotomous nature and be logical in its division. Students may begin by first classifying obvious characteristics, such as color and markings, followed by more specific characteristics, such as physical differences among structural characteristics.

Analyze and Conclude

1. A dichotomous key leads you in classifying an organism in a timely, logical way, allowing you to classify it step-by-step with each characteristic. A book would probably only give descriptions of each organism. You might have to read a long time before you found the organism you were looking for. Keys are most useful for quick identification in the field.

2. Students' answers may vary. Any answer is acceptable as long as it is logically supported. Most students will probably think that a dichotomous key could be used to classify nonliving items, as long as the items have characteristics that can be classified.

Reinforcement and Study Guide
Page 105 • Section 17.1

1. d
2. f
3. a
4. e
5. b
6. c
7. genus
8. true
9. true
10. common
11. true
12. true
13. can
14. birds
15. true
16. species
17. kingdom
18. order
19. species
20. order, class, phylum, and kingdom
21. The mountain lion and the domestic dog are most closely related because they belong to more of the same taxa (four) than the other animals do: Kingdom Animalia; phylum Chordata; class Mammalia; and order Carnivora.
22. phylum Chordata and Kingdom Animalia
23. Amphibia
24. order: Primates; family: Hominidae; genus: *Homo*
25. The organism belongs to the genus *Rana*, family Ranidae, order Anura, class Amphibia, phylum Chordata, and Kingdom Animalia.

Reinforcement and Study Guide
Page 107 • Section 17.2

1. Structural similarities between groups of organisms suggest that the groups evolved from a common ancestor.
2. Organisms that show different breeding behaviors are of different species.
3. Similar species that are found in the same isolated geographic area probably evolved from the same ancestral species.
4. Groups of organisms that are closely related to each other show similarities in the number, structure, and DNA sequence of their chromosomes.
5. The more closely two groups of organisms are related, the more their DNA nucleotide sequences and their proteins are similar.
6. theropods, *Allosaurus, Sinornis, Velociraptor,* and *Archaeopteryx*
7. *Sinornis*
8. light bones, three-toed foot, wishbone, down feathers, and feathers with shafts, veins, and barbs
9. Unlike a cladogram, a fanlike diagram shows when groups of organisms evolved and the relative number of species in each group.
10. arthropods
11. sea stars
12. d
13. d
14. b

Refuerzo y Guía de estudio
Página 109 • Sección 17.1

1. d
2. f
3. a
4. e
5. b
6. c

7. género

8. verdadero

9. verdadero

10. comunes

11. verdadero

12. verdadero

13. se pueden

14. las aves

15. verdadero

16. la especie

17. el reino

18. el orden

19. la especie

20. el orden, la clase, el filo y el reino

21. El puma y el perro doméstico son los animales con relación más cercana porque tienen más taxones en común (cuatro) que el resto de los animales. Los taxones comunes son: reino Animalia; filo Chordata; clase Mammalia y orden Carnívora.

22. el filo (Chordata) y el reino (Animalia)

23. Amphibia

24. orden: Primates; familia: Hominidae; género: *Homo*

25. El organismo pertenecería al género Rana, familia Ranidae, orden Anura, clase Amphibia, filo Chordata y reino Animalia.

Página 111 • Sección 17.2

1. Las similitudes estructurales entre grupos de organismos sugieren que dichos grupos evolucionaron a partir de un antepasado común.

2. Los organismos que tienen diferente comportamiento reproductor pertenecen a diferentes especies.

3. Las especies similares que se encuentran en una misma área geográfica aislada, probablemente descienden del mismo antepasado.

4. Los grupos de organismos estrechamente relacionados muestran mayores similitudes en el número, estructura y las secuencias de DNA de sus cromosomas.

5. A mayor cercanía entre grupos de organismos, corresponde una mayor similitud en las secuencias de los nucleótidos del DNA y en las proteínas.

6. teropodos, alosauros, *sinornis, velociraptor* y arqueópterix

7. *Sinornis*

8. huesos livianos, pies con tres dedos, espoleta, la presencia de plumón y la presencia de plumas con cañones, venas y barbas

9. A diferencia del cladograma, el diagrama de abanico muestra cuándo aparecieron los diferentes grupos y el número relativo de especies en cada grupo.

10. a los artrópodos

11. las estrellas de mar

12. d

13. d

14. b

Concept Mapping
Page 113 • Classifying Organisms

1. Eubacteria

2. prokaryotes

3. unicellular

4. autotrophs or heterotrophs

5. Archaebacteria

6. Protista

7. unicellular or multicellular

8. autotrophs or heterotrophs

9. Fungi

10. unicellular or multicellular

11. Plantae

12. eukaryotes

13. autotrophs

14. Animalia

15. eukaryotes

16. multicellular

17. heterotrophs

Critical Thinking
Page 114 • Organizing Life's Diversity

1. The dog and the tuna; their amino acid sequences differ only by four amino acids.

2. More similar to a tuna; in the amino-acid sequence shown, a moth's amino acid sequence differs from a tuna's by only seven amino acids. It differs from wheat's by nine amino acids.

3. No; on the diagram, turtles are more closely related to birds than they are to snakes.

4. the kangaroo

Teacher Guide & Answers

Section Focus Transparency 41
Page 115 • Classification

Purpose
- To introduce the concept of classification

Teaching Suggestions
- Before projecting the transparency, ask students what kinds of music they listen to. Then ask how they find the music they want when they go to a music store. Project the transparency, and draw attention to the signs that indicate the different kinds of music.
- Ask students how knowing in which section of the music store an unfamiliar CD is located would be helpful in gathering information about the CD. (By knowing in which grouping the CD is, you know that the music on the CD has certain characteristics.)
- Ask students how grouping living things might be helpful. Lead students to understand that by grouping or classifying organisms, scientists can see the relationships among them more easily.
- *Answers to questions on the transparency include:*
  1. The music is grouped according to its type—classical, country, rock and roll, and new age.
  2. It is easier to find particular CDs in the store.

Section Focus Transparency 42
Page 116 • Classifying Organisms

Purpose
- To illustrate that organisms can be classified according to similar characteristics

Teaching Suggestions
- Project the transparency, and ask students to describe the characteristics of each animal.
- Have students classify the animals according to similar characteristics.
- After students have classified the animals into groups, introduce an additional animal, such as a horse, and ask students how they would go about deciding in which group to place the animal. (Match the characteristics of the additional animal to the characteristics shared by a particular group.) Ask students what they would do if the additional animal did not fit in with any of the existing groups. (Reclassify the organisms into different groups or create a separate group for the additional animal.)

- *Answers to questions on the transparency include:*
  1. Groupings will vary, but animals within each group should share distinctive characteristics.
  2. Answers will vary according to classifications used.

Basic Concepts Transparency 24
Page 117 • Life's Six Kingdoms

Purpose
- To infer from a fanlike diagram the evolutionary relationships among organisms.

Teaching Suggestions
- Project the transparency. Begin by reviewing the names of the six kingdoms of organisms. Ask students to give examples of members of each kingdom. Then have students use the diagram to identify the order in which the six kingdoms and some of their subgroups evolved.
- Make sure students understand that modern taxonomy depends less on apparent similarities in physical structure and function than on evolutionary relationships. For example, bats, birds, and butterflies have wings and fly, yet they are classified in distinctly different phyla by virtue of their evolutionary differences.
- Emphasize the point that the complexity of organisms varies directly with their position on the evolutionary tree—that is, the most complex organisms, such as mammals, evolved most recently.

Extension: Reading
- Have students read Lynn Margulis's book, *The Five Kingdoms*, which includes eubacteria and archaebacteria as part of one kingdom, Monera. Although much of the book may be too difficult for most of your students, it describes and illustrates each of the kingdoms very well. Students will find a vast number of interesting details in this book.

Answers to Student Worksheet
1. Kingdom Eubacteria
2. mammals; about 245 million years ago
3. flowering plants
4. Protists may be the evolutionary ancestors of plants, animals, and fungi.
5. ferns
6. jellyfishes and sponges
7. Kingdom Animalia; Kingdom Archaebacteria
8. The cells of organisms belonging to Kingdom

Eubacteria and Kingdom Archaebacteria are prokaryotic, whereas the cells of all other organisms are eukaryotic.

9. The basis for classification in the six-kingdom system is phylogeny, or evolutionary relationships.

Reteaching Skills Transparency 26
Page 119 • Six Kingdoms

Purpose
- To differentiate between each of the six kingdoms of life
- Skill: Classifying

Teaching Suggestions
- Explore with students the various ways that people divide living things into groups. (Students are probably most familiar with the groups insects, animals, and plants.) Discuss the way that biologists divide living things into very inclusive categories called kingdoms, then subdivide kingdoms into smaller and smaller groups. Explain that in this section students will learn about the broad characteristics of the kingdoms. Subsequent chapters will include more details about the kingdoms.
- Present the transparency, and have students identify the kingdom to which each organism belongs. (methanogen: archaebacteria; *E. coli:* eubacteria; *Euglena:* protists; bracket fungus: fungi; tomato: plant; giant squid: animals) Then have students fill in the chart on their worksheet.
- Review the distinguishing characteristics of each kingdom.

Extension: Research
- Have students select a specific type of archaebacteria, research it, and report on its adaptations to its environment.

Answers to Student Worksheet

1. a. Eubacteria: prokaryotes (no membrane-bound nucleus); microscopic; unicellular; strong cell wall; genetic makeup less complex than that of eukaryotes; live in most environments that are not extreme
   b. Archaebacteria: prokaryotes (no membrane-bound nucleus); microscopic; unicellular; genes have a similar structure to those in eukaryotes; live mostly in extreme environments—salt lakes, swamps, deep-ocean hydrothermal vents

   c. Protists: eukaryotes (membrane-bound nucleus); unicellular and multicellular; some plantlike, some animal-like, and some fungus-like; lack complex organ systems; live in moist environments
   d. Fungi: eukaryotes (membrane-bound nucleus); do not move from place to place; unicellular or multicellular; heterotrophs that absorb nutrients from organic materials in the environment
   e. Plants: eukaryotes (membrane-bound nucleus); stationary; multicellular photosynthesizers; most have chloroplasts and cellulose cell walls; cells are organized into tissues that are organized into organs and organ systems
   f. Animals: eukaryotes (membrane-bound nucleus); multicellular; heterotrophs; no cell walls; most can move from place to place; cells are organized into tissues that are organized into organs and complex organ systems

2. Differences in cellular characteristics and methods of nutrition
3. Archaebacteria and eubacteria live in very different environments. Also, their cell membranes, cell walls, ribosomal RNAs, and their genetic makeups differ.

Chapter Assessment
Page 121 • Reviewing Vocabulary

1. d
2. e
3. a
4. h
5. b
6. c
7. g
8. f
9. d
10. c
11. c
12. b
13. a
14. b

Page 122 • Understanding Main Ideas (Part A)

1. environment
2. true
3. species

4. a genus

5. genus

6. fewer

7. true

8. true

9. Eubacteria

10. true

11. protist

12. bacterium

13. fungus

Page 123 • Understanding Main Ideas (Part B)

1. Answers may state that Aristotle's system didn't account for animals that live in more than one kind of environment, nor did it show evolutionary relationships among organisms.

2. Answers may vary. Scientific names use Latin words, which do not change and are recognized by scientists all over the world. The use of scientific names avoids confusion where there is more than one common name for an organism. Common names can be misleading in terms of what an organism actually is. Scientific names reflect how organisms are related to each other.

3. Differences in cellular characteristics and methods of obtaining food are used to distinguish kingdoms.

4. a. prokaryotic

   b. eukaryotic

   c. eukaryotic

   d. eukaryotic

5. a. unicellular

   b. unicellular or multicellular

   c. unicellular or multicellular

   d. multicellular

6. a. heterotrophic or autotrophic

   b. heterotrophic

   c. autotrophic

   d. heterotrophic

7. a. no

   b. no

   c. yes

   d. yes

Page 124 • Thinking Critically

1. *Vulpes velox* is a species of fox because it is of the same genus as the red fox, *Vulpes fulva*.

2. kingdom: Animalia; phylum: Chordata; class: Mammalia; order: Carnivora; family: Canidae; genus: *Vulpes*; species: *V. velox*

3. The dog and the wolf are most closely related because they have the greatest number of levels of classification in common, differing only at the species level.

4. Gophers and house cats share the same kingdom, phylum, and class; they diverge at the order level.

5. A dog, a red fox, and a house cat share the same kingdom, phylum, class, and order. However, dogs and foxes are in the same family, whereas dogs and cats are not.

Page 125 • Applying Scientific Methods

1. Hybrid A

2. Hybrid B

3. The radioactivity level would be higher at 85°C. Because Hybrid A has a high proportion of matched sequences, it has a higher melting temperature; thus, single strands containing radioactive iodine would not be present at lower temperature.

4. Answers may vary. The birds in group A are more closely related to the birds in group C and should be classified together.

5. Mix radioactively labeled, singled-stranded DNA from birds in group A with unlabeled, single-stranded DNA from birds in group C to form hybrid DNA. Then determine the proportion of matched sequences by measuring levels of radioactivity in the filtrate as the hybrid DNA is heated in stages. Then repeat the experiment using DNA from groups A and B and compare the results.

6. The independent variable is the two types of bird DNA (group A, B, or C) that are mixed. The dependent variable is the proportion of matched sequences in the hybrid DNA.

7. The control would be mixing labeled DNA from birds in group A with unlabeled DNA from birds in the same group.

Student Recording Sheet
Page 127

Answers can be found on page 464 in the Teacher Wraparound Edition.

BioDigest 5

Reinforcement and Study Guide
Page 129 • Change Through Time

1. Precambrian
2. Prokaryotic cells and first eukaryotic cells evolved.
3. Paleozoic
4. Ferns and conifers appeared; worms, insects, fishes, and reptiles evolved.
5. Mesozoic
6. Reptiles diversified; mammals and flowering plants evolved.
7. Cenozoic
8. Primates evolved.
9. nonliving material
10. controlled experiments
11. biogenesis
12. protocells
13. 2
14. 4
15. 1
16. 3
17. Relative dating assumes that in undisturbed layers of rock, the deepest layers contain the oldest fossils.
18. Homologous structures are similar anatomical structures in different organisms that might indicate possible shared ancestry.
19. false
20. true
21. true
22. false
23. true
24. d
25. a
26. e
27. c
28. b
29. kingdom
30. Lynx rufus

Refuerzo y Guía de estudio
Página 131 • Cambios a través del tiempo

1. Precámbrico
2. Aparecen las primeras células procariotas y eucariotas.

3. Paleozoico
4. Aparecen los helechos y las coníferas; aparecen los gusanos, los insectos, los peces y los reptiles.
5. Mesozoico
6. Se diversifican los reptiles; aparecen los mamíferos y las plantas con flores.
7. Cenozoico
8. Aparecen los primates.
9. la materia inanimada
10. experimentos controlados
11. la biogénesis
12. protocélulas
13. 2
14. 4
15. 1
16. 3
17. Se asume que en estratos de roca no perturbados, las capas más profundas contienen los fósiles más antiguos.
18. Son estructuras anatómicas similares que presentan diferentes organismos y que indican la posible existencia de un antepasado común.
19. falso
20. verdadero
21. verdadero
22. falso
23. verdadero
24. d
25. a
26. e
27. c
28. b
29. el reino
30. *Lynx rufus*

Student Recording Sheet
Page 133

Answers can be found on page 470 in the Teacher Wraparound Edition.